Suicide Intervention Handbook

LivingWorks

Suicide Intervention Handbook

Visit LivingWorks Education's website for more information on suicide intervention
and promoting suicide-safer communities: **www.livingworks.net**

ISBN-0-9698448-1-6
Printed in Canada

Richard F. Ramsay, MSW
Bryan L. Tanney, FRCP (C)
Wm. A. Lang, PhD
Tarie Kinzel, BScN, MEd.

Editorial Support
Lois Lang

Roger J. Tierney, PhD (in memory)

LivingWorks

suicide-safer communities · saving lives for tomorrow

LivingWorks Education Inc.
4303D 11 Street SE
Calgary, Alberta T2G 4X1
Telephone: (403) 209-0242
Fax: (403) 209-0259
E-mail: info@livingworks.net
Website: www.livingworks.net

This handbook is based upon an original version created for The Office of Prevention, California State Department of Mental Health. That version was published in 1990 as the California Helper's Handbook for Suicide Intervention. We wish to thank David Neilsen and other members of the "California team" for their help in getting this all started. The first edition, published in 1994, was a major modification of the original publication. Minor changes were made between the first and second editions. The tenth edition has undergone extensive change in format and content. Well over 200,000 copies of all previous versions are in circulation.

Table of Contents

1 introduction

introduction

This handbook provides help in meeting some of the challenges of reducing suicidal behavior. The first chapter is an overview. It shows how the information in the handbook can help with the goal of creating life-assisting communities — communities that are safer from suicide. We organized this chapter around some questions people might have about suicide. One or more of them may be similar to concerns you have. Read them first. They are shown in the "thoughts" graphics. The regular text following the graphic is how we think the handbook can be used to help you with your concerns.

Sure, suicide is probably another important thing to learn about but, really, is suicide that big a problem? I think I should just walk on by.

-AN INQUIRING MIND

Don't do that. Suicide is one of the most underestimated community health problems in the world. More people are dying from suicide than in all of the armed conflicts around the world and about the same or more than those dying from traffic accidents. For every person who dies by suicide, there are as many as 100 times more people who injure themselves from nonfatal suicidal behaviors. In any year, approximately 6% of the entire population has serious thoughts of suicide. Four to five percent of all people attempt suicide in their lifetime; one in nine have seriously considered suicide. Since suicide affects people at all ages, the loss in potential productivity is staggering. The emotional costs of any suicidal behavior, although not as measurable, are even more staggering. The legacy of suicide is often a lifetime of grief, sadness, anger and confusion.

Preventive Education

I don't know why I picked up this book. Strange that I just remembered that guy on the basketball team who died way back in high school. That was a suicide, wasn't it? At any rate, I don't know anything about suicide. I am curious. I wonder if this book will have anything for me, or will it be too complicated?

-AN INTERESTED PERSON

Yes, this handbook has something for you. Some parts may go into greater depth than you are interested in at this point but you may also discover that you are more interested than you thought. We tried to write it so that any interested person, with or without formal training, could benefit from it. You might want to have a look through the quick reference at the very end. It provides an overview of the handbook. You might also want to start with the second chapter on attitudes about suicide. When it comes to suicide, attitudes are very important. Another starting place is the true and/or false checkup at the end of each chapter. There, you can check your understanding of the information in the chapter. When you don't know the answers, the information in the chapter will likely be new to you. Following the checkup in the third and fourth chapters is some additional content designed primarily for readers with a more specific interest. You may — or may not — find that material a bit technical. Parts of Chapter 5 might seem that way too.

It is great that you are curious. Some remain unaware of how a big a problem suicide is and why prevention activities are so important. Others recognize the problem and are searching for ways to play a role in making suicide less likely. An informed community is also more likely to support other activities that make for a life-assisting community. You will discover more about those as you move through this handbook.

We hope the handbook will help you feel more informed about suicide. Who knows where that feeling might lead you? As you will learn, there are many places and ways for you to become involved.

Suicide Intervention

Finally I have the time to have lunch with Bob. We are all just so busy. I wonder how he is doing with his divorce? Never did think they were suited. Bob says, "Jim, thanks for coming. I have a favor to ask. I wonder if you would be the kid's godfather and the executor of my will? I hope you say yes. It is the last thing I need to do before ending all of this." ::

I can tell he wants to talk. The way he is hanging around. I know my son. He doesn't talk as much now that he is older but at least he still comes to me. I'll just be patient, sooner or later, he will say what is on his mind... Your son says, "Mom, you would be okay, wouldn't you, if I wasn't around any more?" ::

Let me see, who is next? Oh, Mary. Yes, she seems to be doing so much better. Each week she seems to have more things sorted out. [You signal to the receptionist to let Mary in.] Uh oh, I have never seen her look so bad. Worse than when she was talking about suicide. ::

All the teachers are talking about it. Ed's suicide has got them all worried. We are supposed to be on the lookout for kids at risk — just one more responsibility. But, what should we be looking for? And what would we do if we found someone? ::

-CAREGIVERS FACED WITH INTERVENTION SITUATIONS

Have you been in any of these situations? This handbook is primarily for those who have. Are you the kind of person other people turn to when they are having troubles? If yes, this handbook is also for you because, sooner or later, you may have a similar chance to help save a life.

Chapters 3 and 4 talk about and give examples of how you might intervene to help prevent the immediate risk of suicidal behavior. Chapter 3 focuses upon identifying persons at risk and reviewing how and why they are at risk. Chapter 4 provides a step-by-step overview of how to do an intervention and includes several examples.

Chapter 2 will help you explore your attitudes about suicide and helping persons at risk. It will help you to recognize if any of your views might make it difficult for you to provide a first-aid intervention. In an emergency situation, you do not have time to discover which of your own attitudes and beliefs about suicide might be helpful and which might be a problem.

The final chapter is about a community-wide approach to suicide prevention. Knowing the number of different activities and resources that together help to create a coordinated life-assisting community may encourage you to get involved.

Suicide Case Management, Treatment and Therapy

The immediate suicide danger is over, at least for now. But how do I help this person to deal with the problems that brought him to consider suicide in the first place? Who else needs to be involved in the helping process? How do we go about working together?

-CAREGIVER DOING ONGOING HELPING

This handbook is useful for those who have ongoing responsibilities for helping persons who are at risk. Using your case management, treatment and therapy skills, you assist in resolving the problems that brought the person to consider suicide. At the same time, you can use the risk review, safeplan and other suicide intervention strategies outlined in this handbook to monitor and protect against suicide risk.

Postvention

I get the feeling everyone is waiting for me to say what to do. It goes with my job after all. But I can hardly believe it happened. I knew that student. Suicide was not a word I would have ever thought to use in the same breath with his name. But, here it is. I feel like running away from it but I also know we need to do something.

-A PERSON IN A LEADERSHIP POSITION AFTER A SUICIDE

Before it happens, every caregiver needs to think about what they will do after a suicide. Avoidance of suicide is common, so you may feel ill prepared for this situation. While Chapter 5 in this handbook only touches briefly on helping after a suicide, it does provide an outline of some of the things you might want to consider. At the end of the handbook are references to more complete sources of information for developing appropriate policies, procedures and protocols.

Community Coordination

I am sick and tired of seeing these kids kill themselves. I am sick and tired of seeing suicide, period. We don't have any programs for preventing suicide, for dealing with people who have thoughts of suicide, or for responding after a suicide. The community is not talking about it, much less working together. We need some talk and some planning.

-A CONCERNED COMMUNITY MEMBER

The major headings in this chapter are some of the important elements in creating a suicide-safer community, such as community coordination for example. The following figure shows how these elements fit together. Imagine a river where the conditions become increasingly more serious as one moves from the upstream "contributaries" of suicide, downstream into the main body of the river of suicide where the person is thinking about suicide and on toward a dangerous waterfall where a person acts upon their thoughts of suicide. The aim of prevention is to help people avoid having thoughts of suicide—avoid getting into the main river, in other words. The aim of inter-vention (coming between thoughts and acts) is to help people out of the river of suicide and back into the community. Postvention is for persons harmed and affected by the suicidal behavior. Persons affected by a traumatic event may need help to work their way through the experience or else they may be at increased risk. Longer-term therapy may be needed to help a person injured by suicide move back into the community. Community coordination helps resources to work together. You will find other ideas for helping your community become a suicide-safer community in Chapter 5.

Suicide-Safer Community
Preserves, protects and promotes life

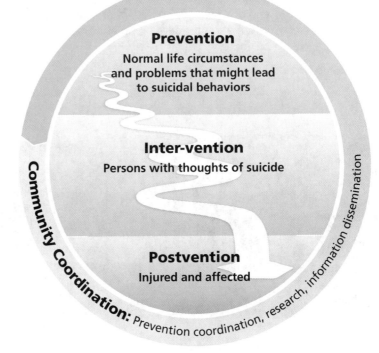

Prevention
Normal life circumstances and problems that might lead to suicidal behaviors

Inter-vention
Persons with thoughts of suicide

Postvention
Injured and affected

Community Coordination: Prevention coordination, research, information dissemination

Getting Help For Yourself

I don't know how all of this got started. Problems started building up and then I found that I was thinking about suicide. I wonder if there is anything in here that can help me?

-A PERSON AT RISK

If someone were to ask you right now if you were having thoughts of suicide, right now, what would your honest answer be? If yes, this is surely a difficult time for you. There is no reason for you to have to go through this alone. Find someone to help. Doing so is an act of wisdom and courage — and relief, as you find someone to share the distress and the struggle. The information in this handbook will tell you something about what kind of help is available and what that helping might involve. While the handbook is mostly written from the helper's point of view, we have outlined some of the most important points for you to consider in the next paragraph.

> **Suicide is not the only way out.**
>
> Likely, you have already realized that having thoughts of suicide is a serious matter. Being alone with thoughts of suicide is one thing that is known to increase the risk of harm or death. Find someone who is comfortable talking about suicide — someone who will work with you to prevent the risk of these thoughts leading to suicidal actions. One of the quickest and best ways to find out if your helper has these abilities is to tell them that you are having thoughts of suicide and watch their reaction. They may not be comfortable immediately, but expect them to show more concern for you than themselves. If they don't measure up to this standard, there are others who will. Keep trying. Once you have found someone, don't expect that the helper is going to keep the danger secret or not want extra help. You want a helper who is honest about how much they can do. Lastly, be honest. Don't say anything just to please the helper and never promise anything you won't or can't do. Everyone needs to take the time to find what will really help. Suicide is not the only way out.

You may have read this section out of general interest and not because you are currently thinking about suicide. Informing persons at risk about how to get help is part of suicide prevention. Informing everyone about how to get help is also part of suicide prevention. Suicide is part of the human condition: anyone could find themselves with thoughts of suicide.

The Fine Print

This handbook makes good sense. Not too much technical language; lots of hints and a number of examples. I can use this. I can think of a number of uses for it: a textbook for teaching suicide intervention, a desk reference for all kinds of caregivers, an introduction to suicide safety. We could also use it to…

-A HAPPY READER

We hope you will be pleased with the handbook but we don't want you to get carried away with that feeling. There are two important limitations.

The handbook focuses upon things that are likely to apply in almost any suicide situation. Such suggestions are always general in nature. Although there are recognized common elements in suicide intervention, not enough is known about suicide to be very specific. One of the most important general rules to remember is that every suicide situation and every person at risk is unique. You will need to trust your own judgment and adjust your approach to fit the particular situation. A good way to remember this idea is frequently to say to yourself, "but it might not always fit every situation or person."

The second limitation may not be as obvious until you have finished the handbook. When you begin to put it all together and think about what being a suicide first-aid caregiver means, we suspect you are going to recognize that you do not feel as ready, willing and able to undertake that role as you would like unless you have already completed *ASIST* or a program like it. We hope you will take that recognition as a valuable insight and not as a failing — on your part or ours. This handbook is primarily an introduction to suicide intervention. While we believe you will find this handbook helpful, it will not prepare you to be a suicide first-aid caregiver.

As a simple way of explaining that more is involved, the content of this handbook is part of the participant materials for the two-day, *Applied Suicide Intervention Skills Training (ASIST)*. For those of you who don't know about *ASIST*, it is a two-day, hands-on, highly interactive, practice-oriented program led by registered trainers working with no more than 15 participants per trainer and no fewer than two trainers. In *ASIST*, this handbook's contents helps participants finalize the things that were learned first-hand, learn more about some topics and refresh learning at a later date. If you want to feel ready, willing and able to be a suicide first-aid caregiver, plan to attend an *ASIST* or something similar.

1   This handbook doesn't cover everything involved in creating a suicide-safer community.

True. It is mostly about suicide intervention.

2   A suicide-safer community includes prevention, treatment and therapy, help after a suicide and community coordination.

True, but a trick question. It also includes emergency first-aid intervention.

3   If suicide prevention were 100% successful, there would be no need for the other aspects of suicide safety.

True, but almost a trick question. If every suicide situation is different, imagine all the possible causes of suicide that a suicide-safer community would have to do something about. There is not enough knowledge (or money) to do that. A significant number of people will be missed by our best prevention efforts, making the other aspects very important.

4   Preventing people from ever having thoughts of suicide seems like an overwhelming task.

True and False, in some ways it is an overwhelming task, as the previous answer indicates. A more realistic goal would be for communities to support programs that help people develop resiliency in dealing with life's difficulties. With this internal resource, suicidal thoughts are less likely or more manageable. Resiliency to suicide might include problem-solving and coping skills as well as knowing what to do and who to contact should suicidal thoughts occur.

5   Suicide intervention is for situations in which a suicidal behavior is in progress.

False. Despite how useful it is to compare immediate suicide intervention to CPR, there is sometimes a problem with that comparison. The ideal in suicide intervention is to recognize the presence of suicidal thoughts early and prevent suicidal behavior from happening.

6   This handbook was mainly created to introduce intervention principles.

True. While there are many people who will find this handbook useful without attending an intervention skills training workshop, this handbook is not a substitute for that training.

7   This handbook covers just about everything involved in working face to face with persons at risk.

False. There are many books about working with persons at risk, particularly on an ongoing basis. Many practical approaches to managing continuing risk are known. There are also theories that show ways to transform suicide risk into a life-changing and life-embracing process.

8   It might be dangerous to speak directly to persons at risk, as you do in this handbook.

False. Silence and secrecy are the allies of suicide. Talk and openness are the keys to a life-assisting community. If you want to know more about this, read the next chapter.

9   I can learn almost all I need to know about suicide intervention from this handbook.

False. You will discover this yourself. You need at least two additional things that this handbook can not provide: 1) an open environment in which to fully explore your attitudes about suicide with other concerned people; and, 2) practice, and seeing other people practice, doing suicide interventions.

2 connecting

connecting

Suicide is still a hidden or taboo topic. Denial, secrecy and avoidance remain common. While we no longer kill the person who fails to complete suicide or the family of those who do, avoidance of a person with thoughts of suicide can be as deadly a punishment as execution.

The taboo surrounding suicide and the stigma clinging to those who experience it has been with us for a long time. Both can influence the feelings of caregivers toward working with persons at risk in powerful and often hidden ways. They come to life as notions about suicide: ideas or beliefs that support denial, secrecy and avoidance. The purpose of this chapter is to help you connect with your attitudes about suicide. This will help you overcome notions or feelings that might hinder your willingness and ability to help. Clarifying your own attitudes about suicide and learning to listen to the attitudes of others are important caregiver skills. An intervention situation is not the time to try to figure out what you believe or to hear a person at risk express attitudes about suicide that you have not thought about before.

Attitudes Over Time

The existence of suicide is at least as old as recorded history. This mode of death has been noted in almost every culture and in every era. Societal responses to suicide have varied tremendously throughout history — heroic, honorable and a duty; acceptable as an act of faith or patriotism; subject to punishment as a mortal sin, crime or sign of madness; and, today, more a multi-caused condition requiring help.

Pacific Islanders agreed with suicide for those who violated tribal taboos. Among certain Inuit groups it was said to be the custom for the elderly and disabled to kill themselves to relieve the burden on their families. Suicide among tribal peoples is often associated with outside intervention and breakdown of their culture. For the Incas and other South American natives, suicide was connected to their fear of conquest. Native peoples of Africa killed themselves to avoid slavery, and North America's Indians and First Nations peoples were known to have done the same to avoid living on reservations.

In ancient Asian and Oriental cultures, Confucianism, Buddhism and Shintoism accepted euthanasia and suicide in cases of incurable illness. Hinduism allowed suicide in rare situations. Hindu Brahmins believed that suicide assured a direct route to heaven and it was not uncommon for widows to kill themselves following the death of their husbands in a practice known as *sati*. In China, suicide was viewed favorably after defeat, financial ruin, dishonor or the death of a spouse. In Japan, ritual suicide known as *hara kiri* was accepted, and in some cases expected, in situations involving dishonor such as being taken as a prisoner.

Suicide was quite common in ancient Greek and Roman civilizations, but there were several schools of thought ranging from disapproval (Pythagoreans), to conditional acceptance (Epicureans) to approval (Stoics). Acceptance and approval was associated with avoidance of capture, slavery, and murder or to express a higher ideal. Among the casualties of these attitudes were Demosthenes, Socrates, Hannibal, Brutus, Anthony and Cleopatra.

In ancient Israel, suicide was taboo but exceptions were allowed to avoid capture and deal with a serious sin. Suicide is uncritically mentioned several times in the Old Testament. Samson killed himself in the process of slaying the Philistines. Saul fell on his sword rather than be taken captive. Judas Iscariot's death is the only mention of suicide in the New Testament. In Judaic history there are several reported incidents of mass suicide. Nearly 1,000 people killed themselves at Masada in 73 A.D. to avoid capture and enslavement by the Romans. Five hundred reportedly completed suicide to escape oppression in 1190 in York, England.

Early Christianity viewed suicide as acceptable martyrdom. As it grew into the dominant religion in the Roman Empire, suicide was labeled a sin and a secular crime, perhaps to try to stop the large numbers of deaths occurring by martyrdom. By the 6th century St. Augustine was the first Christian to make a blanket condemnation of suicide. What he meant to be a humanitarian position and to show respect for the sanctity of life, declined into legalized acts of atrocity toward the suicidal person and their families.

In the Middle Ages, the criminalization of suicide was at its worst. The bodies of people who killed themselves were dragged through the streets, hung naked upside-down for public view, and impaled on a stake at a public crossroad. In England, the surviving families of persons who killed themselves were severely stigmatized. The widow(er) and children were formally censured, the family's property was confiscated, and the body was denied burial in the church or city cemetery.

By the sixteenth century, the philosophies of ancient Greek and Roman societies were beginning to be rediscovered and the unconditional condemnation of suicide was questioned. In Holland, suicide was argued to be a defense for an unendurable life situation. Attitudes in the eighteenth century started to see laws against suicide become less brutal and shift in the direction of viewing a suicidal person as suffering from an illness and not as persons committing a criminal act. Yet in places like England and other countries, it was not removed as a crime until well into the twentieth century.

Early in the twentieth century, condemnation began to be replaced by an emphasis on trying to understand suicide. Suicide came to be viewed as one outcome of social, psychological and biological forces over which the individual may have little control. This change led to a more humane approach to the prevention of suicide. One result was revoking laws that made suicide a crime in the hope that those at risk might be more encouraged to seek help. At the same time, restrictive laws against aiding, abetting and counseling suicide were passed in many countries. Legal support of involuntary detention of persons at risk continues to be a common prevention tool in most countries. In the last half of the century, more tolerant views emerged, as reflected in the debate over physician-assisted death and euthanasia.

This historical mixture of attitudes coupled with the increasing diversity of modern culture makes agreement about suicide and its prevention very unlikely. Different points of view occur from one person to another, one institution and organization to another, one subgroup of a culture to another. All of this diversity is also found between and within caregivers —— and in persons at risk. For every individual, suicide produces a wide mixture of responses, often occurring at the same time. In particular, sharing past personal experiences with suicide can be very uncomfortable. With this potential for controversy, confusion and emotional upset, suicide remains a difficult topic for discussion even today.

Notions About Suicide

Common notions or ideas that people have about suicide are often a reflection of much older societal views. They remain current because they provide reasons for not talking about or getting involved with the issue of suicide. Some are so deeply a part of our beliefs that we do not recognize that there is little evidence or logic to support them.

On the following pages, in the left-hand margin, are some of these "mis-ideas" that we have called **notions**. Below each notion, in the "stop sign," is the **avoidance** that the notion supports. In the text are some suggested antidotes that can be used to counteract the notions and help you move past these barriers to helping. When you find yourself trying to defend such notions or feeling uncomfortable about your reaction to the antidotes, we encourage you to ask yourself whether what you are thinking, feeling and doing is based upon denial, secrecy or avoidance. Better still, start a discussion about attitudes with others.

Most suicides are caused by a single traumatic event.

The things that cause suicide happen so fast and are so powerful that no one can do anything to stop suicide.

ANTIDOTE

A sudden, painful event may set off or hasten a decision to die by suicide, but it is unlikely to be the only cause. More typically, other contributing events and feelings have occurred over a prolonged period of time. There are often a number of opportunities to do something helpful. We need to recognize the stressful events and the person's feelings about and reactions to them as invitations to get involved. Even when a very big loss happens suddenly, there is still much that can be done to prevent suicide. With help, human beings are capable of withstanding almost any kind of loss.

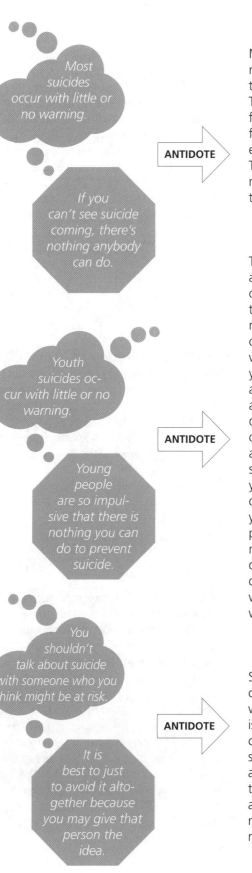

Most people communicate how they are reacting to or feeling about the events that are drawing them toward suicide. These communications — or invitations for others to offer help — come in the form of direct statements, physical signs, emotional reactions, or behavioral cues. They telegraph the possibility that suicide might be under consideration as a solution to difficulties in their life.

The teen years and early twenties are a time of great change. The biological changes that come with puberty lead to experimentation with new roles and responsibilities. Youth may appear to be constantly changing but this is seldom without thought or purpose. While youths in general may be more prone to act hastily than adults, that is not true of all youth. Young people who act unpredictably often have a well-known history of other risky behaviors such as substance abuse, reckless driving or unprotected sex. Even for this minority group of youth, considering suicide is a very serious undertaking. Most often, signs that a youth is being drawn toward suicide are present. It may be more work to recognize their invitations to help, but that does not mean that they are not being offered. If you make a connection, you will be able to recognize a young person who is at risk.

Serious talk about suicide does not create or increase risk. It reduces it. The best way to identify the possibility of suicide is to ask directly. Open talk and genuine concern about someone's thoughts of suicide are a source of relief for them and are often the key elements in preventing the immediate danger of suicide. Avoidance leaves the person at risk feeling more alone and perhaps too anxious to risk asking someone else to help.

connecting

> *Youths are at much greater risk of suicide than any other age group.*

> *We only need to pay attention to youth suicide.*

ANTIDOTE

All ages are at risk of suicide. In the 70's and 80's, the rate of suicide for youth did increase faster than that for the general population. Recently, that trend appears to be leveling off with the youth suicide rates becoming similar to all other ages. In some places, suicide among people in their thirties and forties and in the elderly occurs at a higher rate. While attending to youth suicide risk is vital, it can obscure the fact that all ages are at risk of suicide.

> *People who talk about suicide won't do it.*

> *There is no need to get involved with people who talk about suicide.*

ANTIDOTE

People who attempt suicide usually talk about their intentions, directly or indirectly, before they act. Most people who die by suicide talk about it in some way with another person before they act. Not taking this talk seriously may be a contributing cause in many deaths by suicide.

> *A nonfatal outcome means it was only an attention-getting behavior.*

> *These behaviors can be ignored.*

ANTIDOTE

Nonfatal suicidal behaviors are often a desperate invitation for others to help the person at risk live. Such behaviors demand attention. If help is not offered, a person at risk may reach the conclusion that help will never come. Not taking them seriously may actually increase their reasons for dying. Punishing someone with suicidal thoughts or actions as if they were using an improper way to invite help can be very dangerous. Punishment often has the opposite effect to what we want. Help with problems, as well as help in finding ways to ask for that help, is far more likely to be effective in reducing suicidal behaviors.

> **Persons who are really serious about dying choose very lethal methods.**

> **Those who plan to use methods that may not kill them don't need to be taken seriously.**

ANTIDOTE

There is a modest connection between how much a person wants or intends to die and the method they use but other things also influence their choice of methods. People tend to choose a method that they feel comfortable with or they make the choice for some other personal reason. Everyone thinking about suicide should be taken seriously. Anyone who has chosen a specific method should always be protected from using that method. People sometimes kill themselves in ways that you might have thought were impossible.

> **Suicidal persons want to die.**

> **There's no point in helping; they will just keep trying until they die by suicide.**

ANTIDOTE

Most suicidal people are unsure about dying right up to the point of acting. Part of them wants to die, but part of them wants to live. Very few are absolutely determined or completely decided about ending their life. Most people are looking for help to avoid suicide, even if they aren't immediately aware that they want help. The vast majority of people who are suicidal at some time in their life find a way to continue living.

> **All persons who suicide are mentally ill.**

> **By treating mental illness we can get rid of suicide.**

ANTIDOTE

While there is a fairly strong correlation between many mental illnesses and suicide, not all people who suicide are mentally ill, nor are all who are mentally ill likely to die by suicide. While treating mental illness is a worthwhile activity, even very successful treatments will not prevent all suicides among the mentally ill. Also, such a treatment approach would be inappropriate for and therefore offer nothing to the many people who are not mentally ill but who are at risk of suicide.

connecting

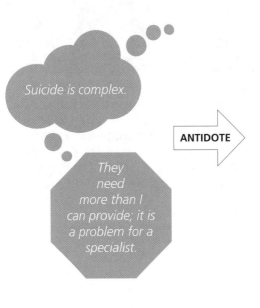

Once a person attempts suicide, she won't do it again.

I don't need to be concerned now; the attempt will be cure enough.

ANTIDOTE

Although it is true that most people who purposely harm themselves do not go on to kill themselves later, a significant number who attempt will attempt again. The rate of suicide for those who have attempted before is 40 times higher than that of the general population. Because this difference in the rate of death by suicide is so great, prior suicidal behavior is a major risk factor.

Suicide is complex.

They need more than I can provide; it is a problem for a specialist.

ANTIDOTE

As is true of most human behavior, fully understanding suicide is very challenging. General rules that apply to all persons at risk are not possible. It might even be said that there are as many reasons for suicidal behaviors as there are people who engage in them. In this sense, specialists don't always know what to do either. Understanding and responding to thoughts of suicide in a particular person, however, is no more complex than understanding and responding to any other aspect of a person's behavior. It is the possibility of suicide that sometimes makes caregivers forget what they know about helping. It may be useful to remember that the vast majority of people who consider suicide never harm themselves. While specialist care can be helpful, many persons are lost to suicide because things that helpers could do, such as emergency first aid and immediate support, either were not offered or were not available.

Feeling better could mean two quite different things: a decision for life, as one would hope, or increased danger because the person has made a decision to die and is no longer in emotional conflict about deciding. A person who is severely depressed, for example, may not have the energy to kill herself. A lifting of the depression may provide the energy needed to act. Open and direct discussion of suicide is the only way to determine whether a lifting of mood is a sign of progress or of even greater danger. Without this direct questioning, resources that support progress or worse, resources that protect against danger, may be withdrawn before they should.

People at all social and economic levels have comparable rates of suicide. Each individual's view of their life situation is a far more important element in the decision to suicide than any general social condition. There is no group label that will help you quickly, or with any certainty, identify those who might be at risk; just as there is no one solution for helping every person at risk to decide against suicide. Each has their reasons for suicide. With your help, each can find their way to continue living.

Suicide is a choice anyone can make, although almost no one wants to be suicidal. At least 4% of the population will intentionally harm themselves in their lifetime. Many more will seriously consider suicide. Suicide is part of the human condition. However, most people who think about suicide never act on the idea. Most people who consider suicide only have this happen once in their lives. Your efforts to help may be enough to support a person through a difficult and dangerous period.

Most people at risk are desperately looking for another way out of their situation. Labeling people at risk in such a negative way serves only to make it harder for them and for other persons at risk to reach out for support. Since no one is completely safe from the possibility of suicide, the "give what you want in return" principle applies: do unto others, as you would have others do unto you.

People who kill themselves are taking the easy way out.

ANTIDOTE

These people do not deserve any help; society is better off without them.

Suicide is rarely selfless. Survivors of suicide often struggle with its impact for the rest of their lives.

Suicide is rarely a person's preferred choice. The decision for suicide may be made in the midst of many turbulent feelings and is seldom the result of informed decision-making about all of the possibilities. Most persons at risk are unsure and want to talk to someone. A person at risk who makes a strong point about their right to suicide may well be telling you how uncertain they are about dying. Similar statements on a helper's part are often a reflection of their own uncertainty about helping.

Suicide is an individual choice.

ANTIDOTE

It is none of my business.

Caregiver Reactions

If any of the previous notions — or some version of them — are a part of your beliefs about suicide, your readiness to help a person at risk is likely impaired. Even when someone willing to help has been freed from most of the common notions about suicide, more personal beliefs and feelings may still hinder one's readiness and ability to provide first-aid help. Some of the more common reactions that impair readiness to provide first-aid are reviewed in this section. After each, suggestions for dealing with them are offered. You may find yourself defending these reactions as inevitable or unmanageable. We encourage you to question whether what you are feeling might be based upon or supported by denial, secrecy or avoidance. Better still, talk about your reactions with others.

PANIC

I feel helpless and inadequate in this situation. I'm just a friend (a teacher, a parent, etc.); I'm not a trained crisis worker.

It might seem frightening, but you can help. Suicidal individuals seek out those whom they trust and feel connected to in some way. One of the most important factors in preventing a suicide is the presence of a supportive resource. Many suicidal periods are short-lived. By talking and listening, you may draw the person into a supportive relationship with you and away from self-destructive thoughts. You are also providing a safe period of time in which other forms of assistance can be mobilized.

FEAR

What if I try to help, and she does it anyway?

There is no point in avoiding this possibility. While it may be helpful to remember that the person is ultimately responsible for their own decisions, knowing this is not likely to counteract the painful feelings you will experience if they attempt or complete suicide. Shock, anger and sadness are some of the many normal emotions of grief and loss experienced by anyone near a suicide. Always talk to someone. Don't let the taboo about suicide affect you too.

FRUSTRATION
I don't have time for this right now. Surely it can wait. I have a schedule to keep.

Effective interventions can be short-term and time-limited. What a person at risk usually needs most is someone to connect with now — when the feelings of helplessness and hopelessness are strongest. If a caregiver can provide this connection, it will often help the at-risk individual to look beyond the immediate situation. Other solutions can then be generated and put into action, and other resources mobilized. If you have now become aware that a person may need help with suicide, now is the time to help.

ANGER
How much more am I expected to do as a friend (a teacher, a parent, etc.)? Now I've got to be a helper too! How dare you do this to me?

While this anger may feel justified now, it won't last if you miss the opportunity to help and a person injures or kills themselves. Typically, such anger is covering up for feelings of inadequacy or frustration about how well a helper believes they can deal with the situation. If this is the case, you are better off to acknowledge these feelings. Honest self-talk will free you to be more effective during the intervention or to find other help for the person at risk if you feel you cannot help.

RESENTMENT
I'm being used and manipulated with this attention-getting behavior. It doesn't seem that serious to me.

Helpers charged with the responsibility of looking after the welfare of others can expect to be frustrated at times. The additional responsibility of protecting against the risk of suicide can seem like more than they should have to bear. One way to protect against the frustration is to view thoughts of suicide as a form of manipulation. Helpers charged with looking after youth, for example, might tend to minimize the importance and intensity of adolescent feelings and fail to recognize a young person's crisis. The threat of suicide, however, is more an act of desperation than it is an act of manipulation. Communicating suicidal thoughts is often a cry for help. Any statement or threat about suicide must be taken as a serious invitation that demands a constructive reply.

HELPLESS

Her situation is hopeless. How am I ever going to find anything that will make this person want to live?

Don't get lost in all of the problems that brought the person to consider suicide. Focus on finding ways to avoid suicide at this moment. Other problems can be dealt with later. Take one step at a time. The passage of even a short period of time safe from suicide can make a significant difference.

HOPELESS

If I were in a similar situation or condition, I would probably consider suicide too. I don't see any other choice available to her.

It is important to recognize and understand your own attitudes about suicide. It is equally important to recognize that your attitudes may not be the same as those of a person at risk. Just because you believe, for example, that terminal cancer might justify suicide doesn't mean that a person thinking about suicide who also had a terminal illness does not need your help. Most important is helping the person at risk to sort through their issue(s). Remember, if they are talking to you, they have not fully decided to die. Knowing what you might do in similar circumstances is important for understanding yourself, but more often than not, irrelevant to the needs of the person at risk.

CONFLICTED

If a person really wants to kill themself, no one has the right to stop them.

This reaction frequently occurs when a helper is trying to decide whether or not to get involved. By focusing on their own beliefs about individual rights, the helper misses the fact that the person at risk is undecided about dying. If they wished, the person at risk could conceal their intention to die. If they are talking to you, they are undecided. They want to talk. To respond with "you have the right to do whatever you want" is to miss (dismiss) the invitation to talk. It is possible to respect the needs and views of a person at risk while still showing leadership in providing options for safety and support.

Despite your best efforts to stay with the process of working with the person at risk, there may be rare situations in which your respect for the rights of the person at risk comes into conflict with your desire to prevent suicide. Everyone's prevention commitment has limits. These limits differ from helper to helper, and often change over time. Some helpers have ethical guidelines or institutional policies that help them to make decisions in this situation. No helper should ever feel that she must make such a decision alone. After you have found other help for the person at risk, talk over your feelings with others.

Caregiver Attitudes

Attitudes consist of basic feelings and emotionally charged ideas about who we are, the way the world is and the way we believe both should be. It is helpful to reflect on how these feelings and beliefs have been shaped by our own experiences and to recognize that others' experiences may lead them to a different view. Our attitudes shape, and then explain, how we feel about and respond to things in the world. They are the power in our character that informs and guides what we do. The range of positive characteristics and attitudes that could aid an intervention, if not unlimited, is at least very long. Patience, persistence, tolerance, respect, understanding, empathy, intuition, thoughtfulness and practicality come immediately to mind, but one could easily start with passion, idealism, faith, hope and compassion. There is no magic list.

Sometimes willpower alone is enough to find the means to accomplish a goal but knowing how to do something strengthens willpower. Knowledge helps to scatter the common notions about suicide that impair our readiness to help. Self-knowledge helps us set aside those things within us that may hinder helping relationships and make it difficult for us to attend to the needs of a person at risk. Knowledge of how to do an intervention helps to put aside will-draining feelings and to tap into the positive feelings that support our intervention efforts. When helpers have both the will and the knowledge, they have the potential to be ready, willing and able helpers.

1 Helping a person at risk requires the skills of a professional helper.

False. This is another notion. If you are willing and know something about first-aid, you can make a big difference — whether you are a professional helper or not. You are only doing the first-aid part. If you feel you need help after that, get it.

2 Culture doesn't always get it right.

True and False. The original leaders of our culture, who shaped our beliefs, wanted to prevent suicide. In using denial, secrecy and avoidance, they got their methods wrong. It is equally true that people create cultural beliefs, as much as culture creates people's beliefs. If we want culture to use more effective methods, we need to help change the culture.

3 Any person with thoughts of suicide should be taken seriously.

True. Thoughts of suicide can be just a moment from suicidal behavior. Even persons with little intent to die are swimming in a dangerous river. Persons who choose less dangerous methods can still die by those methods.

4 It is not so much that suicide is hidden, as that we hide it.

True. Once you know how to look, the invitations to help are usually very evident. Adopt denial and avoidance, and you can be deadly surprised.

5 You can tell who might be at risk just by knowing if they belong to a higher risk group.

False. There is some useful information on high risk groups (see the next chapter). If you use that information as your only means of recognizing persons at risk, you will miss people who are at risk and you will falsely identify a lot of people who aren't at risk.

6 A person at risk clearly wants to die, chooses a method that works quickly and does not let anyone know what they are planning.

False. Such a person likely does not exist, although a very few may come close. Most are ambivalent, choose a method for personal reasons, and invite help in a number of ways.

7 The antidotes (in brackets) for each of the following caregiver reactions are: calm (panic), confident (fearful), satisfied (frustrated), focussed (angry), purposeful (resentful), active (helpless), resourceful (hopeless), decided (conflicted) and resolved (troubled).

False. These could be the corrective opposites but so could others. Each person puts the world together in different ways. There is no magic list of attitudes or characteristics that will work in every intervention situation. Use your own; they will work.

8 Once you understand that attitudes can affect your intervention behavior, you pretty well know all you need to know about attitudes and suicide.

True and False. Once you recognize how attitudes can blind and misdirect you, you have a powerful tool for putting your best effort forward. On the other hand, people and suicide are complex. You will never stop learning new things about life and about yourself.

true and/or false

3 reviewing risk

reviewing risk

Suicidal behavior is like a river running through your community with a dangerous waterfall at the end. There are some signs warning about the dangers of going into the river, but strangely the riverbank is not marked nearly as well as the community's roads and highways. Whenever someone deliberately enters the river, they take the risk of being swept over the waterfall to their harm or death.

Your job as a community helper is somewhat like that of a lifeguard. It is to spot people in the river as quickly as you can, get them to the bank and get additional help before they reach the waterfall.

If we knew why people ignore the prevention signs in the first place or exactly what causes them to "jump in," we could make the necessary changes to make our communities suicide-safer. This might require a dam upstream or barricades erected all along the riverbank. Unfortunately, the exact causes of suicide are not known. There is no single or perfect prevention plan. Despite the best of prevention efforts, some people will always enter the water and knowingly place themselves at risk.

Imagine a part of the river is entirely open to our view, where we can see right across and for a distance in both directions up and down. If a suicidal person came into this part of the river and was fully determined to go over the waterfall — a rare state — they would conceal their distress, swim quickly downstream and hide from view whenever necessary. Far, far more likely, they will be moving slowly, sometimes fighting hard against the current, and calling out— inviting us to help. This may seem strange. Even though they have entered the river, there is some part of them that wants to get out — wants to go on living. These invitations for help may not always be clear or loud, but the more we know about listening and watching for these invitations to offer help, the better we will be able to recognize and respond.

A community helper needs to be good at: spotting these invitations to help; reviewing the risk of harm or death once it is known that suicide is involved; and developing a contract to reduce the immediate risk. These three tasks — recognizing invitations, reviewing risk and contracting a safeplan — are covered in this chapter. In the next chapter, these three tasks are put together with three other intervention tasks.

Recognizing Invitations

Recognizing that the things that you see, hear and sense might be invitations to help prevent suicide is part science, part practical knowledge, part intuition and in part, just plain willingness to be open to the possibility.

Scientific knowledge about groups at risk

People with certain characteristics are known to be more likely to have thoughts of suicide than others.

Least useful

As noted in the previous chapter, suicide rates are comparable across socioeconomic groups. While certain occupations occasionally show higher rates of suicide, this relationship is often weak and, over time, often inconsistent so as to be of little value in recognizing when a particular individual might be at risk. Rates of suicide are higher in isolated rural regions and lower in suburban areas perhaps because rural areas have fewer resources or people in rural areas have less access to them. Changes in such factors as general economic conditions, social stability and the attitude of society towards suicide occasionally show some relation to suicide. Monitoring these changes may help us know when rates might go up or down in general, but they will not help us to recognize risk in individuals. Environmental factors such as seasons of the year, phases of the moon, day of the week, time of day or climate, show little or no consistent relationship with suicide — certainly none of practical value to caregivers.

Age and gender

Age and gender show some relationship to suicidal behavior but in very inconsistent ways. Completed suicides are approximately four times more common among males than among females. However, females are far more likely to engage in nonfatal suicidal behaviors.

Age patterns are almost as complex. Consider, for example, youth suicide. Suicide is the second leading cause of death among teenagers and young adults in Canada, the United States and Australia. Only accidents take more young lives each year and some of these may actually be suicides.

In Canada, approximately 700 young people (15 to 24 years of age) kill themselves annually. That works out to almost two deaths a day. In the United States approximately 5,000 young people die annually: 14 per day. In Australia, over 300 in this age group die per year. In all three countries, the suicide rate among adolescents and young adults tripled between 1960 and 1980 (1990 for Australia). The dramatic increase in self-inflicted deaths among these age groups accounted for almost the entire increase in the rate of suicide in the general population.

Older people also complete suicide at a somewhat higher rate than the rest of the population. Older citizens tend to suffer a loss of resources that can lead to isolation and loneliness. Their powers of perception decrease. Personal health often worsens. Their self-respect and self-esteem may be undermined by a combination of societal pressures and physical changes. Older people often experience feelings of uselessness and hopelessness. They have serious depressions more commonly than young people and these depressions are often not diagnosed and/or treated.

Despite somewhat higher rates for older persons, particularly older males, the rates of suicide for all ages are more similar than different. For nonfatal suicidal behavior, the relationship is clear: youths have much higher rates. In the United States Youth Risk Behavior Surveys funded by the Centers for Disease Control (CDC) consistently find around 20% of teenagers attending school reporting they have seriously considered suicide in the previous 12 months. Ten to 15% of the surveyed students report they have actually attempted suicide in the previous 12 months. These surveys are based on random or census samples of school populations in grades 9 through 12 and are conducted every two years at state or school board levels. Sample sizes are usually large enough that the results are considered to apply to the entire population of students within the survey boundaries. Comparable percentages of youth suicidal behaviors have been reported in both Australian and Canadian studies.

If you are beginning to suspect that using age and gender information to identify persons at risk could be confusing, you are right. For completed suicide, males in all age groups are at greater risk. Although older persons usually have slightly higher rates, males and females at all ages are at more or less equal risk. Young females, and to a lesser degree young males, are at a greater risk of nonfatal suicidal behavior than their counterparts in older age groups.

Actually, the problem is far bigger than remembering all of the variations. There is no way to tell, upstream in the river, whether a person is headed toward suicide or nonfatal self-injury. Because age and gender give conflicting or inconsistent information about which ages and/or genders are more at risk of either outcome, it would

reviewing risk

be dangerous to use these features as aids in predicting injury or death due to a suicidal act. The best and safest conclusion is that all ages and both genders could be at risk of suicidal behavior, fatal or nonfatal.

Marital status

There is a fairly consistent pattern regarding marital status for the three countries for which there is long-term data: Australia, Canada and United States. Married or partnered individuals are at lower risk; single, separated/divorced and widowed individuals are at higher risk. Underlying this pattern may be such factors as loss, aloneness and/or the presence or absence of personal resources.

Gays, lesbians and bisexuals

Gays, lesbians and bisexuals are more at risk of nonfatal suicidal behavior than their heterosexual counterparts. Surveys conducted in the 1990's in the United States consistently report youth with homosexual orientations to be at two to three times greater risk of nonfatal suicidal behavior than their heterosexual counterparts. These random and census sample surveys provide reasonable support to several earlier studies that compared relatively small adult samples that identified themselves as homosexual with control groups. The risk is considerably greater for teenage gay/bisexual males than their lesbian and heterosexual counterparts. Studies in Australia and Canada report similar results. A school board survey in Seattle showed greater risk of nonfatal suicidal behaviors for heterosexual youth who were harassed for their perceived homosexual characteristics. The risk appears to be higher when individuals, especially teenage males, begin to acknowledge their sexual orientation. As with most persons at risk, isolation and discrimination likely play an important role in the suicidal behavior of lesbians, gays and bisexuals.

Minority groups

In general, first generation immigrants tend to have suicide rates similar to those in their country of origin. However, the stress of acculturation and of isolation due to language and other barriers can contribute to increased risk for these groups of people.

In the United States, the suicide rate among young African-American men is lower than for Caucasians, but it has tripled for males and doubled for females in the past 25 years. Nearly half of all African-American suicides occur in the 20 to 34 age group. The rate of reported suicides for Hispanics is lower than that for Caucasians or African-Americans. Like African-Americans and Native Americans, it is most common in the 20 to 24 age group. This is especially true for males. For Hispanic women, suicide rates are highest in middle age. Comparable data on African-American and Hispanic groups in Canada is not available.

Suicide rates for Aboriginal/Native persons in North America are approximately three to four times that of the general population, with most of this difference resulting from the suicidal deaths of young

Aboriginal/Native males. Some Aboriginal/Native communities have very low rates, while others have rates that are tragically higher than the average. Suicide in Aboriginal/Native groups appears to be related to a complex interaction between socio-cultural forces, isolation, depression, and substance abuse. Available data indicates that Australia's Aboriginal peoples have much higher rates than the rest of the population.

Persons in jail or prison

People in prison are at higher risk than the general population. Inmate suicide rates can be as much as three to four times greater than comparable age and gender groups in the general population. While inmate populations tend to have other high-risk characteristics, such as a history of suicidal behavior and mental disorders, it is clear that there is something uniquely stressful about being in prison. The times immediately following an arrest or after a transfer from one institution to another appear to be the most dangerous. It is worth noting that greater control, including control over suicide means, does not by itself protect against risk. The intervention process, examined more fully in the next chapter, emphasizes the importance of obtaining the cooperation of persons at risk in any plans to prevent suicide.

Mental disorders

Most mental disorders are associated with an increased likelihood of self-harm or suicide. Having more than one mental disorder makes the risk even higher. The Depressive disorders (bipolar, major depression and dysthymia) have the strongest relationship to suicide. Many of the identifying features — such as sadness and apathy, self-blaming, hopelessness, loss of interest in activities, insomnia, and loss of appetite — are prominent among the signs for suicide. Schizophrenias are another disorder associated with suicide. Persons with either of these chronic and severe disorders are often inadequately treated. This is very troubling as there is growing evidence that treatment for these two mental disorders reduces the risk of suicide.

Certain ways of living accompanied by distress and dysfunction are named personality disorders and several of these (antisocial and borderline) are linked to suicide. As another example, the connection between suicidal behaviors and alcohol and other substance abuse is strong. In most studies, about one-half of all completed suicides were associated with legal intoxication at the time of death. Those with a history of chronic alcohol dependence are about four times more likely to die by suicide than the general population. A problem with substance abuse either currently or in the past significantly increases the odds that a person with any other mental disorder will die by suicide.

CAUTIONS

Caution and judgment are required in applying any of this information. Consider depression, since it has the strongest connection with suicide. Not all persons who end their lives by suicide are depressed.

Information about the connection between depression and suicide can lead to an "only those who are depressed are suicidal" fallacy. Knowing that a person is depressed increases vulnerability to suicide, but its absence cannot be used to rule out risk. As the risk recognition and review framework that we will explore shortly indicates, determining risk involves more than diagnosing a mental disorder.

Another misuse of such information is the "all those who are depressed are suicidal. Not all persons who are depressed have thoughts of suicide. Most don't, in fact. Identifying everybody in any high-risk group as suicidal would eventually exhaust caregivers who would, literally, be running around trying to intervene where suicide often did not exist. The risk recognition and review framework to be explored shortly is the key to solving this "false positives" problem — telling who among a high-risk group is at risk and who isn't.

Another, and perhaps the greatest misuse of a connection like that between depression and suicide is the notion of "assumed causation." Knowing that two things are connected does not tell us how they are connected. It is wrong to assume that depression causes suicide. Where depression is present, it may not be a major factor for that person. When it is a major factor, there are many ways it could affect the person. Depression could operate chemically to make a desire for life difficult to sustain. Living with depression, like any chronic problem, can be a "depressing" existence and lead to the gradual loss of one's desire for life. The first onset of depression could frighten one into suicide. So could a further episode after many years of good health. The stigma and taboo of having a mental disorder can become unbearable. It is also possible that thoughts of suicide might contribute to depression, or that both are actually caused by some other unknown factor or factors, or unknown factors that differ from individual to individual.

The motivation to do something about suicide often comes from persons who are part of or concerned about a specific at-risk group who are identified by feature X. Unfortunately, what begins as a willingness to get involved and help is often undermined by the assumption that only special efforts can meet the needs of group X. This assumption is a direct descendant of the third notion ("X causes suicide") and is inconsistent with what is known about suicide. Such efforts create a climate that actually encourages the first two notions just discussed ("only those who are or have X are suicidal" and "all those who are or have X are suicidal"). The best information we have at present is that each individual's reasons/motivations/causes for suicide are numerous and more unique than similar to any other person's or certainly to any group's characteristic.

> **"**
> avoid an over-reliance on any particular theoretical perspective
> **"**

Many of the approaches to understanding human behavior have been applied to understanding suicide. These include, but are in no way limited to, social structures, ego states, thought processes, learning history, self-concept, cognitive development, family dynamics, genetics and personality. More suicide-specific adaptations of these theoretical approaches such as anomie, resiliency, loss and psychological pain have also dotted the theoretical landscape. This theoretical work is essential for the eventual understanding of suicide, but none can come close to claiming the truth about suicide. Unfortunately, intellectual disagreements among advocates of these "grander" theories can be as destructive to unified efforts in preventing suicide as the conflicts that occur among persons concerned about higher risk groups. The prevention of suicidal behavior cuts across disciplines and other traditional boundaries. It requires the efforts of all kinds of people with different backgrounds and different helping experiences. We try to avoid an over-reliance on any particular theoretical perspective. Our ongoing aim is to find terms and concepts that are likely to be understood and used by all caregivers.

The scientific information about groups at risk is best for informing us about **groups** at risk. If you know that someone has a particular high-risk characteristic, you should be more sensitive to any invitations you observe. On the other hand, you should not be insensitive to invitations from anyone regardless of whether or not the person has a high-risk group characteristic.

Information about high-risk groups is primarily useful for planning purposes. For example, from information above it follows that more caregivers with first-aid training might be needed for prison populations. On the other hand, that same information is of no value in determining whom among a prison population is at risk. The methods outlined next work best at finding individuals at risk.

Practical Knowledge About Invitations

Information about invitations collected from people who work with persons at risk is presented just below. The information is of two major types: stressful events involving feelings of loss and reactions to events and life circumstances.

Loss   Stress is unavoidable. It is the response we have to changing events particularly when our resources for coping with the change feel inadequate. Often the events that we experience as negative are most stressful. Since the emotional meanings a person gives to an event arise from their experiences, reactions to stressful events are highly individual. Something that may seem relatively minor to an older adult — the death of a pet, for example — can be taken as meaning, "I can't go on living without the pet" for a younger person or an isolated elderly person. Stressful events that the person feels result in important losses are ones that are most likely related to suicide.

Most people, most of the time, are able to cope with and manage the stresses of life without turning to the option of suicide. They accomplish this by using a variety of internal resources sometimes called resiliency, adaptation or coping, and by drawing upon external resources such as family and friends. Stress becomes distress when these resources are overwhelmed, whether gradually or catastrophically. In such situations, and particularly if stress is viewed as neverending, intolerable or inescapable, thoughts of suicide may arise as a way to relieve the distress. Suicidal behavior becomes more likely when something happens or may happen that produces a sense of overwhelming loss: the "treasured" thing that one had is gone; the thing one always "treasured" is no longer possible.

Losing a parent, spouse or child through natural death, suicide, divorce, or separation can bring about unbearable grief or guilt. Children can lose a feeling of security when they move to a new home or a new school. Adolescents can be traumatized by the breakup of a relationship. Being excluded because of questions about sexual orientation can be experienced as a loss of acceptance. Adults can be deeply affected by career setbacks. Immigrants or refugees often sense a loss of control and predictability, no matter how much the change was desired. The elderly can be overwhelmed by the stress of dealing with retirement or physical disability. Any stress that overwhelms a person's resources, even temporarily, can lead to thoughts of suicide.

Anticipated or potential losses may be just as stressful as actual losses. These might include a fear of failing at school, losing a loved one through divorce, or taking a salary cutback in hard times. Even though the loss hasn't occurred, some people decide that suicide is the only way to cope with a crisis that might occur.

A romantic breakup or loss of a job may mean more than the actual loss. It can be experienced as an intolerable loss of prestige, status, or esteem. For some, it awakens painful memories of earlier losses and raises self-doubt about one's ability to sustain work or relationships. This is especially likely in impulsive young people who may not be fully prepared, psychologically or socially, to cope with losses.

Adults may not be equipped, psychologically or socially, to cope with losses due to past experiences, other current stressors, or mental disorders. Such individuals might be chronically stressed, and more easily distressed because their abilities to cope are limited. Another process for these chronically stressed individual is that stress and distress are more easily aroused in them and can intensify when their ability to cope is limited. They have diminished resiliency because they have fewer resources, cannot access those they do have or their ability to use them is impaired.

The presence of large amounts of stress and/or a number of different stressors does not clearly predict suicidal behavior. There is no certain relationship between the enormity of a particular event and the amount of stress a particular person experiences as a result. The event itself may appear as the precipitating factor that triggers a suicidal behavior, but in most cases it is a "last straw" building on many other background circumstances.

Persons experiencing stress often talk about the stressful events occurring in their lives, perhaps inviting our support to help them cope. Look for life events that involve significant loss. To find out about the severity of the stress, ask directly for personal feelings and the sense of distress they feel about these events.

Reactions When people are distressed they are usually different than when things are going well. A person's thoughts, feelings, behaviors and/or physical functioning may each reveal or reflect that person's distress. Certain of these reactions may also indicate that the person is considering suicide. By allowing you to observe or by sharing them with you, the person may be inviting you to help prevent suicide.

Because so many parts of a person can be affected when suicide is involved, it is helpful to have some way to organize your observations. We have used the framework of seeing (their behaviors and physical changes), hearing (their thoughts and feelings about life and suicide) and sensing (their feelings through the things they share with you) to create the list on the next page. We have added some potentially stressful situations that might result in a person considering suicide to create a "when to be concerned" profile. You might think of these stressful situations as things you learn about by taking an interest in what is happening to the person and how he feels about things.

Learn about SITUATIONS

- relationship problems
- work problems/failing grades
- trouble with the law
- recent suicide and violence, much publicized

almost anything depending upon how the person feels about it

Ask about PHYSICAL CHANGES

- lack of interest/pleasure in all things
- lack of physical energy
- disturbed sleep
- change/loss of sexual interest
- change/loss of appetite, weight
- physical health complaints

Observe BEHAVIORS

- crying
- emotional outbursts
- alcohol/drug misuse
- recklessness
- fighting/law breaking
- withdrawal
- dropping out
- prior suicidal behavior
- putting affairs in order

Listen for THOUGHTS

- escape
- no future
- guilty
- alone
- damaged
- helpless
- preoccupied
- talk of suicide or death
- planning for suicide

Sense FEELINGS

- desperate
- angry
- sad
- ashamed
- worthless
- lonely
- disconnected
- hopeless

Intuition About Invitations

We offer the list as one way of organizing things that can't be organized with certainty. It is not intended to be used as a checklist requiring a certain number of items, or items from several areas to be
present before help is offered. The presence of reactions like those
on the list may not even indicate suicide. Various reactions could
signal that the person has set healthy personal goals and is trying to
make constructive but difficult changes in his life. They could signal
that the person is depressed or mentally ill or that he has another
serious problem but is not thinking of suicide. Just as each person
has a different and unique way of coping with stress, the things that
a person will show or experience when they are considering suicide
vary from person to person. It can be obvious — a note, a direct
statement, an openly declared plan, or an action such as standing
on the ledge of a building. It can be extremely subtle — a gesture,
a posture, a roundabout comment, a tone of voice, or a very small
change from typical behavior.

Awareness of cultural norms may also help a caregiver understand
when an invitation is being offered. For example, averting one's eyes
may signal danger in one culture and be nothing but common practice in another. Gender and age-related expectations within a culture
may also need to be considered.

No general list of invitations will fit all people. Suicidal thoughts will
be detected earlier the better you know or are able to get to know
the person and his typical functioning. You should assume that the
person letting you observe the invitations is giving you permission
to explore what they mean. The more that these invitations point
toward an overall theme involving hopelessness, helplessness and/or
desperation, the greater is the likelihood that they are indicators
of suicide risk. To find out if this theme is present, ask the person
directly if he is feeling hopeless, helpless and/or desperate. Trust your
intuition. If something does not seem right, find out more.

Willingness to Recognize Invitations

If you are truly interested in identifying people at risk, you won't
often have trouble doing it. Whether you remember the scientific
and practical knowledge (and their limitations) or not, whether you
are an intuitive person or not — persons at risk are generally trying desperately to be identified. The greatest barrier to identifying
persons at risk is an unwillingness to do so. Attitudinal barriers like
those reviewed in Chapter 2 and feelings of inadequacy can cause
even the most knowledgeable, sensitive and intuitive to not recognize someone who desperately wants to be identified.

reviewing risk

Reviewing Risk and Contracting Safety

These two tasks will be covered together. There are six risk alerts and there are a number of specific safety elements that need to be done to protect against each risk alert. A risk alert is created when a person at risk confirms certain information about each of six risk factors: thoughts of suicide, planning about suicide, pain, resources, prior suicidal behavior and mental health. Reviewing risk is the process of finding out the information about each risk factor to determine if the information creates a risk alert. Contracting safety is the process of negotiating with a person at risk ways to counteract the risk alerts and keep the person at risk safe. Understanding what the risk factors are and what information creates a risk alert helps in understanding the kind of protective element that is needed. Understanding what the protective element is helps in understanding why the presence of the alert creates risk.

The following figure provides a summary of the risk review factors, the alerts and the protective, safeplan elements liked with them.

REVIEW RISK

RISK ALERT

CONTRACT SAFEPLAN

If thoughts of suicide are present — *suicide* — Keep safe / Safety contact(s) / Safe/no use of alcohol/drugs / Link to resources

Current Suicide Plan
If the person has prepared a suicide plan — *prepared* — Disable the plan

Pain
If the person feels desperate — *desperate* — Ease the pain

Resources
If the person feels alone — *alone* — Link to resources

Prior Suicidal Behavior
If the person is familiar with suicide because of previous suicidal behavior — *familiar* — Protect against the danger/support past survival skills

Mental Health
If the person is vulnerable to suicide because of current or previous mental health concern — *vulnerable* — Link to health worker

Risk Alert 1: Has thoughts of suicide

Even though many persons at risk are desperately seeking help, most will not use the word "suicide" initially. If anything is said about suicide, it will often be done in a roundabout way. Suicide is still a taboo topic and the person at risk is not at all sure what the response to their invitation might be. To find out if a person is thinking about suicide, ask directly. Even if the person at risk does say the word "suicide" directly, confirm it directly by using the word "suicide": "So you are thinking about suicide?"

Asking about suicide does not cause the person to consider suicide if they were not thinking about it or to consider it more seriously if they are having thoughts of suicide. Many persons at risk indicate later that an open discussion of their suicidal thoughts was a crucial part of the helping process.

There are a number of ways to decide when it is appropriate to ask directly about thoughts of suicide. Perhaps you have heard the person say something either directly or indirectly about suicide or death. In responding to this invitation, you might say, "I've heard you mention suicide. Is this something you are thinking about? Are you thinking about killing yourself?"

Perhaps you discover that the person is feeling hopeless and helpless. Here, you might say, "So you are really feeling down. Sometimes when people feel like this, they have thoughts of suicide. Are you thinking of suicide?"

Perhaps you discover that they have experienced what they believe to be a devastating loss. In this situation, you might say, "If I'm hearing correctly, this is the kind of loss that sometimes makes people think that life isn't worth living. Are you having any thoughts like that; thoughts of suicide?"

If thoughts of suicide are present, there is risk that the person may act upon them. The alert is the presence of thoughts of suicide.

Protection for anyone with thoughts of suicide

There are four elements that need to be put into place for every person with thoughts of suicide.

1. A promise to keep safe

Have the person at risk agree not to act upon thoughts of suicide for a specific period of time. The person at risk may think about suicide.

To ask the person at risk not to think about suicide would be virtually impossible and, therefore, dangerous to request. In finding the correct time period, it is usually best to start by asking the person at risk how long they might be able to keep themselves safe. Contracting a keep safe commitment usually sounds something like: "I agree to keep myself safe until after I meet with X. I can think about suicide but I must not act on those thoughts."

2. Provide continuously-available safety contact(s)

Safety contact(s) are backups to other resources in case the person at risk is unable to keep safe and cannot access other parts of the safety plan. The safety contact is either someone who knows that the person at risk might phone or, more usually, it is an agency that regularly deals with suicide situations like a crisis line or a hospital emergency room. You may need more than one resource to ensure 7-days a week, 24-hour coverage. Contracting this element usually takes a form like: "If anything goes wrong and I can't reach anyone else, I will contact X. I will not act on thoughts of suicide, I will contact X."

3. A promise of safe/no use of alcohol/drugs

Alcohol and/or recreational drug misuse or abuse can make suicide much more likely. Access to correct doses of prescription medications must be maintained but protection against overdose should be included. Apart from essential medications, if you can get agreement that all use of alcohol and/or recreational drugs will be avoided, do so. In some situations, such a request might be impossible to follow and, therefore, dangerous to request. In this type of situation, add extra resources to monitor the use or to dispense proper doses of prescription medication. Contracting this element usually takes a form like: "Yes I know that alcohol and/or drugs can be dangerous in my situation. I will follow our plan to avoid them."

> **" alcohol and drugs receive special attention "**
>
> Alcohol and drugs receive special attention because the dangerous effects are so well recognized. While it would be ideal if a person at risk could avoid all use of alcohol or drugs during until the immediate risk has passed, such an aim is likely doomed to failure. Alcohol and drug use of any type is likely a long established pattern, not easily changed while also dealing with suicide. Also, drugs or alcohol use may help to control pain although there may be other ways to accomplish that objective in the immediate context.

4. Link to other resources

Every person with thoughts of suicide should be connected to others who are aware that they are having thoughts of suicide. Usually, more links are better. The type of risk alerts and the availability of resources will determine which links are needed. The more risk alerts, the more likely that formal resources should be included but do not fail to consider informal resources. In these days, quick access to many formal supports is more myth than reality. A caregiver should always think about informal alternatives or supplements. Contracting this element usually takes a form something like: "Yes I agree that I/we/you tell X about me having thoughts of suicide so that they can help if I need it."

TYPES OF RESOURCES	INFORMAL	FORMAL
24-HOUR	family and friends who can stay with the person at risk	emergency
LONGER-TERM	informal advisers (persons who other persons go to)	health workers
LIFE-LONG	personal connections of all kinds	community resources of all kinds

Risk Alert 2: Has a suicide plan — is prepared

Finding out about the plans they have made for suicide helps both you and the person at risk learn how serious they are. Information about plans and preparations tells us how close the act actually is to happening. The more detailed the planning, the more likely it is that suicide has been selected as the only solution. It is also important to realize that a well-developed plan almost seems to demand that it be carried out. Once someone has made a plan, the pressure to finish what has been started can often make completing the plan more likely.

When you want to know about current plans for suicide, ask:
1) how they plan to do it;
2) how prepared they are;
3) how soon it may happen.

Serious planning includes indications that a method and the means to carry it out have been decided, preparations are underway or completed, and a time for action has been decided.

1) **How?** Do they know how they are going to do it? Do they have the means to do what they intend to do? The more specific the decisions, the greater is the risk.

   Do not make any decisions based upon your estimate of the dangerousness of the method. The aim is to prevent death or harm. If they have chosen a method, you need to do something about it even if you think it could not harm them.

2) **How prepared?** Have they made preparations to complete suicide? Has the means been acquired or is it easily available? Has a suicide note been written? Completed preparations and easy access to the means increase the risk of death or harm considerably.

3) **How soon?** Have they settled on a specific time? How close at hand is it? The sooner the person at risk intends to act, the greater is the risk. How long would it take for someone to discover the suicide attempt and try to help the individual? The greater the distance from those who could help, the greater the risk. Persons who indicate that suicide is imminent should not be left alone.

   If the person will not tell you the details of their plan, assume that they have planned in great detail.

✚ Protection against a suicide plan: Disable the plan

When possible, disable the plan and render it ineffective. In the unusual circumstance that a suicide is already in progress, you want to be able to stop it and you may need emergency supports such as emergency medical personnel, or police or security workers. If there is a plan, you need to obtain permission to disable it as part of your safeplan. Disabling one method is no guarantee that a person at risk may not change to other methods but the person at risk's cooperation on this element and all others in the safeplan makes changing methods less likely. If they will not give you the information or the opening you need to disable the plan, the person at risk should not be left alone. You need formal emergency supports. Also remind yourself not to take actions that could risk your own safety.

☞ Risk Alert 3: Has mental pain — is desperate

People vary in their ability to withstand different amounts and forms of pain. For some their pain is very sudden and overwhelming. For others or at other times, the pain is just a dull ache that never goes away. Pain can be either mental or physical, or both. The person suffering from the pain may or may not sense any difference between mental and physical pain. When pain becomes too much to bear, a person might do anything to stop it, whether for a short time or forever. People in this much pain are desperate for relief. Desperation can lead to suicide.

Ask: *Do you have pain that sometimes feels unbearable?*

✚ Protection against mental pain: Ease the pain

Being able to talk with someone may ease the pain. This is particularly true for persons at risk who have not had anyone to talk to about suicide and who are not in physical pain. If talking does not dramatically reduce the pain or the person at risk says that the pain returns periodically, include a connection with a health worker in your safeplan. There may be medications that can help or more frequent "talking" help may be needed.

☞ Risk Alert 4: Feels that they have no resources — is alone

Resources provide protection from being alone. They may consist of family and friends who are likely to be concerned and willing to help. Other external resources that can be supportive include financial security, a satisfying job, a place to live, access to professional help and medical care, positive role models, memberships or access to helpful contacts in church, school, or other social institutions. Any of these can lessen feelings of hopelessness and helplessness. They are tangible life preservers. Their presence makes it less likely that suicide will happen. Their availability increases the likelihood of rescue if a person does make an attempt.

The person most at risk is someone who feels totally alone and cut off from any individual, family, group, community or spiritual connection. They have no one with whom they can discuss their ideas or try out their point of view. During a time of stress, a person without external resources may be very vulnerable. Being alone can also produce mental pain or result in there being no one to talk to as a way to relieve pain, or both.

A person may feel alone because they do not have many resources. More likely, the person is unable to make connections with the resources that they have or that might be available to them. The person at risk may have had bad experiences with certain types of resources in the past. They may feel that certain resources cannot help because they have helped them or others so much in the past and may be exhausted. They may assume that the resources they would most like to turn to would be upset with them for needing their help. It is the person at risk's viewpoint that matters. Their viewpoint is their reality.

Ask: *Do you feel you have few if any resources?*

✚ Protection against feeling alone: Link to resources

We have already included links to resources and a safety contact(s) as part of every safeplan. Certain risk alerts require a link to certain types of resources. Mental pain may require connections with a health worker, for example. Links to resources become even more important for the person at risk who feels alone. They may not actually have or know of any resources, in which case formal resources of some kind are needed. In many cases, resources actually exist but the connection to them is not working. Your primary job for persons who feel alone will usually not be finding resources but re-establishing links to them. If you cannot find a way to re-connect with resources including family and friends, the person at risk should not be left alone. They need emergency supports.

⚑ Risk Alert 5: Has attempted suicide before — is familiar with suicide

The rate of suicide among people who have previously attempted suicide is 40 times greater than the rate in the general population. Following hospitalization for a suicide attempt, dying by suicide is more likely within the first few months of returning to the community. Although the percentage of those with previous attempts who do eventually kill themselves is quite small (10% eventually will), the increased risk is ongoing for many years.

Past suicidal behavior indicates that self-destructive actions are viewed as acceptable and familiar to that individual. Such a history may also suggest that he has difficulty stopping a thought from being directly or impulsively turned into action. The more frequently a person has resorted to suicide attempts as a means of coping with stressful life events, the more likely he will eventually die by suicide.

People typically won't tell you about their previous suicidal behavior without some help. The stigma about suicide is often so strong that even a person who is talking to you about his current suicidal plans might be embarrassed to talk about prior behavior.

Ask: *Have you ever attempted suicide before?*

Does suicide run in the family?

> suicide is a learned behavior

Suicide is a learned behavior. It can be modeled from one generation to another in family settings. Families share and pass on a particular emotional climate that can perpetuate poor coping strategies, feelings of hopelessness, and ultimate self-destruction. A person's risk of suicide usually increases if someone else in the family has ended his life by suicide. There is also some evidence that the experience of being left behind after the suicide of a significant person may actually protect against suicide in the short-term. It is as if one has felt the pain of being abandoned in this way and cannot do it to any other person.

Is the tendency to suicide and other self-destructive behaviors genetic? Can it be inherited? Suicide researchers have reported links between self-destructive behavior, biochemical imbalance, and inherited suicide patterns. Research indicates that a significant number of persons who complete suicide were suffering from diagnosable mental disorders, usually depression. Recent medical research indicates that certain forms of depression are biologically based and are almost certainly passed on genetically.

This does not imply that the children of people who suicide will definitely kill themselves, but they may be more prone to suicidal behaviors than others. Conversely, it does not mean that there is no risk of suicide if there is no family history of self-destructive behaviors.

✚ Protection against familiarity: Protect against the danger; support past survival skills

The influence of prior suicidal behavior is not the same for everyone. In general, the effect is to make future suicidal behavior more likely. The strong relationship between prior behavior and further suicidal behavior supports this general conclusion. Since there is nothing you can do to counteract that influence quickly, extra protection of some kind is needed. If not already included, a link to a health worker may be in order, as may extra immediate protection. On the other hand, some persons may have found a previous attempt to be a turning point toward life. Given an opportunity, they may be able to rediscover lessons in how they got through the previous attempt. The safeplan suggests two activities, one acknowledging the danger and the other reinforcing the potential support from survival skills learned in the past that can be used again. Suggest that if the person at risk does not have past life-protecting skills or resources to rely on, then extra supports and resources are needed. Make a judgment about the influence of past behavior but err on the side of caution. Be careful: it is natural to downplay the power of the past but the past can be powerful.

☞ Risk Alert 6: Has received mental health care — may be more vulnerable to suicide

A mental health concern is any one of several conditions that trained mental health workers can identify. Usually there are characteristic signs and symptoms and often a history of past episodes in the person or in other family members. The conditions are given labels or diagnoses. Of particular importance to suicide are depressions of various kinds, schizophrenias, alcohol and substance abuse, trauma and borderline personality disorders. Knowing the right label helps to find the right treatments. Although the nature of the relationship between suicide and these conditions is far from known, the relationship exists. By association, vulnerability to suicide is higher and special protective elements are needed.

Sometimes the person does not know the actual name of their problem, but can report that they are receiving treatment. If the person at risk names a mental health concern or reports a past or present history of treatment, especially with drugs, a risk alert is triggered. A first-aid caregiver does not need to know about mental health diagnosis or treatment.

Just ask: *Are you receiving or have you received mental health care?*

> **" the stigma and taboo should be resisted "**
>
> There is almost as much stigma and taboo about mental disorders as there is about suicide. Most all evidence indicates that the system of naming and treating mental disorders is practical and generally effective. Within that body of evidence is a known relationship between suicide and most mental disorders. This does not mean that suicide is a mental disorder. Suicide is a choice. On the other hand, getting a mental disorder is, like any illness, largely a matter of no or little choice. The stigma and taboo surrounding suicide and mental disorders should be resisted. The important body of knowledge connecting the two should not be ignored. Using that knowledge might help save a life.

✚ Protection against vulnerability: Link to a health worker

It is good practice to try to connect or re-connect a health worker with any person at risk who is vulnerable. On the other hand, some people cope with a mental health condition quite well or are no longer under its influence. Use the same decision rule as for prior suicidal behavior. Suggest that if the person at risk does not give good reasons to believe there is little effect from this background factor, assume that it has some negative influence.

Conclusion

In this chapter, we have covered what may seem like the heart of first-aid: spotting situations that might involve suicide; determining what is making the situation dangerous; and, finding ways to protect against those dangers. These three tasks do cover much of what a first-aid caregiver is trying to do but they don't cover something very important — the fact that these tasks have to be done with the cooperation of a person at risk. The next chapter covers the process of an intervention: the step-by-step actions of working with a person at risk to prevent the immediate risk of suicide.

1 Information about higher risk groups is more useful for deciding where there will be the greatest need for caregivers. It may not be useful for helping a caregiver to determine the risk of an individual within a particular higher risk group.

True. The risk review framework is the tool for determining whether an individual from a higher risk group is actually at risk at this moment.

2 I was surprised by how few things are known about persons at risk. Obviously not enough money is being spent on research.

False and True. Human beings are complex and we are still learning to understand any aspect of human behavior. On the other hand, research on suicide only began recently and is consistently underfunded.

3 Some things are enough to stress almost anyone.

True, but... Catastrophic events like war or famine impact everyone, but they also often allow people to come together in support of each other while they deal with a common problem. Events that are widely accepted as good or positive events, like winning a lottery, can be a source of tremendous stress for some.
Partly True. When it comes to situations that are more common like moving, divorce or grieving the death of a loved one, it appears that almost everyone is strained by such events. However, the amount of strain and a person's response to it are highly varied and very individual. It is not at all safe to assume that the same events will be stressful for everyone. Look for events that the person feels represent a significant loss.

4 Even the smallest change could be an invitation to help.

True. When someone says, "I might as well be dead," the invitation is obvious. For a person whom you know well, the fact that their eyes don't light up when you ask about their grand-daughter can be just as obvious.

5 A person having occasional thoughts of suicide doesn't neces-sarily qualify as actually having thoughts of suicide.

False. If a person has thoughts of suicide, he is at risk. It is best to assume that the person who has thoughts of suicide is in the river, not stand-ing on the bank having idle thoughts. When you ask a person if they are having thoughts of suicide and they answer "yes," the situation is serious. It demands a suicide intervention.

6 A person with thoughts of suicide would likely need less help if they have: no current plan, no unbear-able pain, no history of mental health concern or no prior suicidal behavior and they feel connected to resources.

True and False. There would be fewer things in the safeplan but thoughts of suicide require a safeplan that has a keep safe agreement, safety contacts, no/safe use of alcohol and drugs and connections to resources informed about the presence of thoughts of suicide.

7	It is important to ask a person at risk how serious he is about suicide.	*False*. A person at risk is not very likely to be able to answer such a general question. What the risk review framework provides are several very concrete and specific questions whose answers will give you — and often the person at risk — a much clearer indication of what things need to be in the safeplan.
8	You just ask the risk review questions and, depending upon the answer, do what the safeplan guide indicates you should do.	*False and True*. Judgment is always required but often what you need to do is just as easy to do as the true and/or false question implies.

Mental Disorders in Risk Review

Mental disorders are patterns of thinking, feeling and behaving that impair a person's normal functioning in society and with other persons. Diagnosing mental disorders is a highly specialized process involving the finding (and not finding) of certain signs and symptoms that tend to go together under a given mental disorder type. There is a significant body of research, often including biological evidence, supporting the distinctions between particular disorders. There is also strong evidence supporting many of the treatment methods that grow out of this framework. The whole system of diagnosis and labeling is under constant review. Although there are problems with this approach and alternatives are available, this diagnostic mental system has much to offer to suicide intervention, due to the information and structure of professional help that has grown up around it.

There is strong evidence that persons with mental disorders are more likely to be at risk of suicide than people in the general population. Any person who has previously been diagnosed with a mental disorder should be regarded as being at increased risk. Some types of mental disorders are more associated with suicide than others and trained caregivers may use this information to refine their risk review. In particular, mood or depressive disorders, schizophrenias, substance abuse disorders and certain personality disorders (antisocial, borderline, cluster B) are clearly associated with self-harm outcomes. It is also well known that having more than one mental disorder, called comorbidity, increases the risk even more. This is especially true when depression or substance abuse is involved.

Information about stressful events and reactions to them takes on new significance when a mental disorder is present. With problems in coping, a person with a mental disorder may be less equipped or able to deal with life's stresses. The disorder itself represents a significant loss — the loss of mental health. Discrimination and stigma, leading to isolation, are common responses to persons with mental disorders. While not a mental disorder, having thoughts of suicide can be very stressful and this might contribute to the onset of a mental disorder.

Inquiries about resources may be different for persons with mental disorders. Many persons with mental disorders may already be well connected or very aware of helping supports in their community. These connections and their knowledge about available resources can be put to good use in developing safeplans. On the other hand, persons with mental disorders may not have as much access to community resources such as family, work mates, neighbors and friends because connections to these natural support networks have been strained or disrupted by the illness. Also, when depressed, people can be less inclined to seek help and less motivated to reach out for, or respond to, offers of support when these are made.

Obviously, gathering information about a history of mental disorders could be very valuable in developing an appropriate safeplan. We wanted to find a way that any caregiver could gather and make use of this information even if they knew very little about mental disorders. To avoid some of the effects of the stigma and taboo that surround mental disorders, we framed the risk review question very carefully: "Are you receiving or have you received mental health care?" We avoided such words as mental disorder, mental illness and treatment to increase the possibility that a caregiver would feel more comfortable asking the risk review question and a person at risk would feel more comfortable answering it. The risk review question is specific enough that a person at risk will know what is being asked if they have or have had mental health care. This phrasing is in no way a sign of giving into the stigma and taboo. Stigma and taboo about mental disorders should be resisted just as much as stigma and taboo about suicide. In a suicide intervention, however, knowing about this risk alert is the most important consideration.

If you find that the person at risk whom you are helping has or has had a mental disorder, assume that a risk alert is triggered. Include a referral to a health worker as part of the action plan. There are two situations that may require some adjustments to this general practice.

1) A person who is already connected with a health worker is being resourceful and therefore is likely to be less vulnerable to suicide than someone who has not made such a connection. Indeed, this is exactly what the framework asks caregivers to do for those who are not already connected. Nevertheless, the important thing for even this more resourceful person at risk is that their health worker be informed about the risk review and safeplan.

2) Some people who sought help at one time may be coping with a mental health condition quite well or no longer have it. The suicide vulnerability alert applies to many persons with mental disorders, but it may not apply to the particular person at risk you are working with or their mental health condition. On the other hand, err on the side of caution. If the person at risk does not give good reasons to assume there is little effect from this background factor, assume that it could have a negative influence. When uncertain, caregivers

should suggest that they do not feel comfortable deciding about the impact of a mental health concern and, thus, the advice of a health worker is required.

Impulsivity in Risk Review

Not all persons at risk invite our help. Some are intent on suicide and do their best to conceal both their planning and signs of distress or desperation. We know that only a small minority of persons who take their own lives belong to this group. The majority offer us opportunities to help them find another way out, and are grateful when we reach out to them.

There is a group of persons at risk for whom the time available to provide help, our "window of opportunity," may be very short. These are persons who think of suicide, decide on self-harm and act on this decision quickly. People who deal with problems this way often have shown similar behavior when called upon to solve other issues in their lives. Acting in this manner is regarded as a stable, ongoing or permanent trait of such people. This characteristic of their temperament or emotional responsiveness is called impulsivity. It can be a dangerous way of responding when thoughts of suicide are also present.

Impulsivity refers to both a pattern of problem solving (acting before full consideration is given to the consequences) and the ability of the person to temper or control emotional responses. In recent years, there has been interest in the biological mechanisms that underlie impulsivity and the part that the brain chemical, serotonin, plays in those processes. People who are impulsive may have learned to solve problems very quickly (sometimes a useful ability) or they may be impaired in their ability to control distressing emotions that mount into desperation very quickly when a solution is less obvious. The origins of these traits may lie in biological processes or in a low psychological threshold of tolerance for painful feelings. There is good evidence that the brains of some people who die by suicide and some people who attempt suicide without much warning have diminished serotonin levels. This understanding has led to attempts to treat persons at risk with serotonin replacement to help keep their emotional balancing system working properly. There are also now several non-biological treatments that appear to help individuals develop psychological tools to tolerate distressing emotions.

It is commonly assumed that youth may be more impulsive. Youth do not have fully developed psychological tools for dealing with emotions. In addition, there is likely a maturation process involved in the development of the chemically-based control system. Caregivers are increasingly recognizing that impulsivity sometimes plays an important part in reviewing risk for individuals of all ages. For all of these reasons we want to provide some guidance on how a caregiver might use this concept in a risk review context.

Obviously, gathering information about impulsivity could be very valuable in developing an appropriate safeplan. We wanted to find a way that any caregiver could gather and make use of this information even if they knew very little about personality diagnosis. We decided to focus upon the interaction between a person at risk's sense of pain and their perception of their ability to manage it. When persons indicate that they do have unbearable pain, the desperation risk alert is triggered. How a person answers this risk review question may be a function of impulsiveness (I can't manage this pain or any distress for that matter) or of intense pain (most all of us

tend to remove our hand from a burning stove quite quickly) or some combination of both. In the risk review framework, it does not matter what the cause of the risk alert triggering answer is. The result is the same: a greater tendency to act quickly. The safeplan counterpart focuses on easing the pain. Impulsivity as a character trait is impossible to change quickly and thus the safeplan focuses on the one element that might be able to be changed — the pain.

Most persons at risk, even the impulsive ones, can agree not to act upon their thoughts of suicide for a set period of time, even though they still have those thoughts. The suicide intervention process is aimed at creating and maintaining this kind of agreement — at providing concrete help for regulating the boundary between thoughts and action for a limited amount of time. Awareness that pain can influence decisions at that boundary should shape the details of the safeplan developed to protect that person during a period of crisis. More concern will likely be given to having readily available access to help when the pain cannot be eased. Time lines for the safeplan are likely to be shorter. More weight is likely to be given to any knowledge the caregiver has of the possibility of additional stress or reactions to stress increasing in the near future. Dealing with persons at risk in great pain also involves the possibility that new or renewed suicidal thinking may occur fairly quickly. In this regard, you may wish to read about "Deciding When an Intervention is Needed" in the Chapter 4 supplements.

Risk Review in On-going Care Contexts

The risk review framework presented in this chapter is the same as that used in the *ASIST* workshop. It was designed to be used in an emergency as part of suicide first-aid. Some participants in an *ASIST* workshop and some readers of this handbook also have responsibilities for the ongoing care of persons at risk. This may include institutional settings such as hospitals or prisons, or an agency that offers extended support.

In an ongoing care setting, risk should be reviewed frequently and repeatedly. Information related to a risk can and does change — and sometimes quite quickly. The following are some questions that might be used as a starting point for gathering information about change in these risk factors:

- **Current Suicide Plan:** Has anything changed about the plan to indicate that the person at risk is more (or less) prepared to suicide?

- **Pain:** Has anything changed that increases (or decreases) the desperation of the person at risk?

- **Resources:** Has anything changed that makes the person at risk feel more (or less) alone?

- **Prior Suicidal Behavior:** Has anything changed that makes suicide more familiar or more acceptable?

- **Mental Health:** Has anything changed that makes you think that referral to a health worker would be advisable?

To our knowledge, the problem of comparing risk reviews over time has never been discussed in the literature of suicide. The following examples outline some of the information that a caregiver might discover as he asks for or thinks about changes in risk review information. They are intended to stimulate your thinking about the value of comparing risk review information over time and about the judgments required in following various lines of inquiry. When risk reviews change, as you will see in the following examples, finding out why they have changed is critical.

Current Suicide Plan

Maybe the person at risk seems to be "burning his bridges" by doing things that cause normal supports to be removed. This might be a signal that the risk is more immediate. Another person at risk may be on "best behavior" and regaining privileges. This may mean things are going better or perhaps it is evidence of increased planning for suicide.

Suppose you discover that another person at risk has changed his suicide plan to a less lethal, immediate and accessible method. This might cause you to think of the risk as lower than before even though a plan is still present. If you knew that the current action plan removed the originally chosen method so that it is no longer available, learning that the person at risk has decided on a different method might cause you to redo your risk review.

Suppose the person at risk now refuses to tell you about the details of his plan. This is often a sign of increased planning and more immediate risk. Suppose that another person at risk appears to be trying to manipulate your risk review to cause you to be less concerned about disabling the plan than you believe you should be. This manipulation attempt may reflect even greater planning than the person at risk who refused to tell you about his plans.

In an institutional context, it is important to recognize that the persons under your care likely know about the institution's standard procedures regarding suicide as well as, or better than, you do. A change in the planned timing of suicide takes on new significance, for example, if you realize that the suicide attempt would now occur at a time when there are few resources available.

Resources

Suppose a person at risk is feeling less alone than previously despite the fact that he has temporarily been cut off from almost all external resources due to a restriction of privileges. When you learn that some persons in the general environment were causing the person at risk distress, feeling less alone becomes understandable. It also becomes clearer that this "positive" change may not last long once relief from escaping these persons wears off.

Prior Suicidal Behavior

It is critical to ask about the impact of recent suicidal behavior by another person in the institution. In considering the impact of a person at risk's own previous suicidal behavior, it is important to learn something about the motivations and context of that history. Knowing, for example, that a prior suicidal behavior was triggered by a visit from a family member takes on significance when you find out that the same family member is visiting again soon.

Mental Health

While a current mental disorder or a history of a disorder found in a previous risk review is likely to have led to an ongoing contact with a health worker, mental health status can change. Persons who did not previously have a disorder could develop one. Persons previously free from a disorder could have it reoccur. Suppose you discover someone who never showed such behavior before, talking to them-

selves and oblivious to everyone around them. Or suppose someone who is normally very talkative is now silent and without any sign of "life in their eyes." While a caregiver may know very little about mental disorders, unusual behavior is not hard to spot and referral to someone who can determine what it means is in order.

Any number of changes or combinations of changes in risk information can occur. There is one clear conclusion from this brief look at possible changes: the more you know about a person at risk, the better your risk review and safeplan can be. A very important conclusion follows that one: the better you document your review and subsequent reviews, the better the risk review and safeplan made by others in your institution will be. To provide some structure to this documentation, we suggest adding the change questions above to the risk review framework with space to note some details on what the changes are, what caused them and what they mean for the risk review and safeplan.

4 assisting

assisting

In this chapter, we offer a model of suicide intervention that has six tasks. Before getting into the details, there are four "big picture" things to keep in mind.

Limited goal

The goal of a suicide first-aid intervention is to keep the person at risk safe from suicide for a limited period of time. We call the agreements between a caregiver and a person at risk that achieves that goal, a safeplan. Suicide first-aid and safeplanning is about now and the immediate future. You don't need to or want to go into the long-term problems and patterns of life that may have contributed to the suicidal ideas or behaviors in the first place. Suicide first-aid is not about life planning: it is about safe planning. Your job is to intervene until the immediate danger or threat of suicide has passed or until additional assistance and resources can be accessed. In this situation, you are a short-term helper, not a long-term therapist. Thinking about it in terms of a person being in the river of suicide, your goal is to help them move to the shore and hang on until they can get out or until other resources arrive.

Repeat as often as needed

You can always intervene again at a later date. An hour from now, a day from now or a year from now you can apply first-aid again to help the same person avoid suicide. Each intervention only needs to prevent the immediate risk of suicide. Perspective is often vital in suicide first-aid. When you intervene with a person whose life really does seem hopeless, even to you, or whom you have helped many, many times before, remember that it was your success at earlier times that allows you the chance to intervene again now.

Involve the person at risk

A third thing to remember is that you want as much work and cooperation from the person at risk as is possible. There will be situations in which a caregiver needs to take a strong leadership role but you also want to respect the person at risk and avoid making decisions for them whenever possible. The safeplan you make with a person

assisting

at risk is far more likely to actually keep the person at risk safe if they have been involved in its creation and fully agree with it.

Any model is only a guide

The fourth thing to keep in mind is that the model is only a guide. Each task has its own goals and objectives, and successful completion of these tasks may require the use of a variety of methods and skills. The way you manage these tasks will unfold differently with every person you try to help. What works with one person may not necessarily work with another, and it may not even work with the same person on another occasion.

Task 1: Explore Invitations

In the third chapter, the idea of invitations was introduced and several ways of recognizing invitations were discussed. There we suggested that a willingness to look for invitations was probably most important. Now it is time to put caregiver action to that willingness. Your first task is to actively explore invitations to see what they mean. Not only does this show caring and concern, it is the best way to quickly find out if the things you hear, see or sense might be connected to thoughts of suicide.

EXPLORE

Connect with the person in a personal way. Explore the situation from their point of view by encouraging them to express their personal concerns. For now, accept their view of their life and recent events without question or argument. Show them that you want to understand their feelings. A focus on things or events that have happened may come first, but events by themselves usually don't bring on a crisis. Crises generally come from the feelings and the meanings that are attached to events. Also when you give a person a chance to fully express their feelings, the distance between you and them will quickly narrow.

There are two objectives for this task:

1) give the individual a sense of acceptance and support;
2) look for signs that suicidal intentions might be connected to the feelings and events happening in their life.

Task 2: Ask about Suicide

As you establish and maintain a connection, you learn more about the person's situation and their thoughts and feelings about it. At some point, you may recognize the possibility that suicide is being considered. You do not need to be sure that such thoughts are present. If there is any possibility in your mind that thoughts of suicide might be present, ask directly about them.

Indirect, roundabout, or unclear questions about thoughts of suicide will often only get you similar answers in return. Be sensitive, but clear and specific. Ask a direct question about suicide. "Are you thinking about suicide?" "Are you having thoughts of suicide?"

There is nothing to lose and much to gain. Being direct and to the point gives the person at risk permission to talk about their suicidal thoughts and possible plans. It makes suicide an issue that can be talked about — instead of a private, hidden problem. Most people thinking about suicide are only too willing to share these thoughts with you. If they are not having thoughts of suicide, explore other ways in which you might help. You no longer need a suicide intervention. If the answer is negative, but offered in some way that makes you unsure of their truthfulness, you should ask about suicide again when further talk reinforces or confirms your concerns. Even if the person does not currently have thoughts of suicide, asking signals to them that you are someone they could talk to about suicide if things changed.

There are two objectives for this task:

1) confirm that thoughts of suicide either are or are not present;
2) show that you are ready, willing and able to help prevent suicide.

Task 3: Listen to the Reasons for Dying and Living

Persons at risk are almost always unsure or ambivalent about suicide. That is, they have some feelings and reasons for dying and they almost always have some feelings and reasons for living. The reasons for dying are usually obvious. Likely they have already talked about them in some way when you were exploring their invitations to help. Part of your job in this task is to help the person at risk express, identify and confirm their reason(s) for dying. Often a good way to start is to connect the things said earlier to the fact that they are thinking about suicide: "Now I understand that the things that have been happening to you and that you are feeling are linked to your reasons for suicide. Tell me more about that."

You don't need to learn all the things in the person at risk's life that they think are related to their current thoughts of suicide. Rather you are looking for a simple, straightforward summary of the most current and pressing reasons. "You can't keep living because..." "It

assisting

sometimes seems like everything is headed toward suicide because..." "What do you think about, see or remember when you think about suicide?" It is often helpful to use such phrases as, "So basically..." or, "In general..." and such time-related phrases as, "Right now..." or, "At this time..."

Persons at risk often want to talk about their reasons for dying. After all, thoughts of suicide are the single, most important thing happening in their lives at the moment. Talking is almost always helpful. Talking involves thinking and thinking may lead to new ways of looking at things. When reasons for dying are put into words, emotions are released and their influence on how a person views events may lessen. The person at risk may for the first time really understand what their reasons for dying are. When a caregiver can reflect back to the person at risk those reasons, the person at risk may begin to see those reasons in a new way. In addition, their sense that you understand helps to build the relationship. Most important, the quickest way (maybe the only way) to get to the life side is to listen to the death side first. The explanation is rather simple and known by all: if you want someone to listen to you, listen to them first. In a way, the ambivalent person at risk is like two people. If you want to help them listen to their life side, show them that you understand their death side first.

LISTEN

In all likelihood, the person at risk has reasons for living or else they would not be telling you that they have thoughts of suicide. They may not know what the reasons are. They may not have even recognized that they have them yet. Once discovered, the reasons may not seem very big or important but even something as seemingly small as wanting to have a reason for living can save a life. Part of your job in this task is to help the person at risk express, identify and confirm their reason(s) for living.

A perfect accounting of all possible reasons for living is not necessary. Try to find the positive tendencies — the personal strengths and

> **"**
> there are legal means to forcibly stop somebody
> **"**
>
> As we all know, there are legal means to forcibly stop somebody from acting on thoughts of suicide in most industrial nations. Persons at risk know this too. When a person at risk lets you know that they are thinking about suicide, they are taking a chance that they may temporarily give up their opportunity to act upon those thoughts. The decision to talk openly with a caregiver is a powerful indication of a desire to live whether or not the person fully recognizes it.

opportunities — in the person at risk and in their situation that still hold the person to life. Focus on those things that are most accessible right now. Identify the feelings that might orient the individual toward a new commitment in favor of life. "Who or what will the person miss the most if they are gone?" "What is the best part of their life?" "How did they solve serious problems previously?" "What would they most look forward to if the immediate pain and problems could be addressed?" "Is there any hope to see if another solution can be found?" "Is there any desire to delay suicide and see if other solutions can be found?" If need be, focus on the fact of ambivalence itself. Since the person is undecided, the best solution is to put off making a decision about suicide until a clearer answer is possible.

Be persistent but don't overdo it. Pulling too hard towards living can backfire and trigger resentment. You want to be flexible as well as persistent. A sensitive introduction of ideas and resources that might sustain life allows both sides of ambivalence to be considered. You are looking for a simple, straightforward summary of the most important, current reasons for living. It is often helpful to use such phrases as, "So basically..." or, "In general..." and such time-related phrases as, "Right now..." or, "At this time..."

Once you have helped a person at risk to, identify, express and confirm their reasons for living, doing something to prevent the risk to life comes to the forefront.

There are three objectives for this task:

1) develop a mutual understanding of the reasons for dying and for living;
2) show respect for the person at risk through your willingness to really listen to them; and
3) establish a life-side foundation for the rest of the intervention.

Task 4: Review Risk

Reviewing risk was covered in some detail in chapter three. In this chapter we fit this task into its place in an intervention.

Most important is to recognize that the word "risk" likely has little meaning to a person at risk until they have actually said what their reasons for living are in their own words. Until the person at risk recognizes that they have reasons for living, only the caregiver views the things that make suicide more likely as risk. Identifying reasons for living comes before risk review, both emotionally and logically. Once there are reasons for living, suicide puts those reasons for living at risk.

Share as much of the risk review process with the person at risk as possible. Start by sharing the reasons why reviewing the risks to life is important: "Okay, there are some reasons to postpone suicide. Now lets look at what might put that goal of staying alive at risk. Let me ask you some questions that will help us to get a good handle on the risk." In most every case, you should share your risk review summary and see if the person at risk agrees with you. The logic behind the risk review framework is pretty compelling even to those who might want to underplay their risk. Be prepared to defend the framework if need be. For example, it is very hard to believe that having a suicide plan, unbearable pain and feeling alone does anything but increase risk. Prior suicidal behavior and a mental health concern might have resulted in some positive learning about survival strategies and produced care and treatment benefits. But also be prepared to point out that persons with prior suicidal behavior and a mental health condition are known to be on average at greater risk.

Obviously agreement about the risk review is vital to the development of the safeplan since the safeplan is directly related to protecting against what is found in the review. Although rare, there will be times when you will need to assume that the person at risk agrees with your review and its related safeplan implications. You might need to be fairly directive because the person at risk can do little more than agree. For example, "I'm concerned about you, John, and I can see that your situation is difficult for you. I want you to see someone right now who can help. I'll phone them now." Sometimes you may even have to speak for life because the person at risk can't. For example, "You let me know about suicide. Some part of you wants to live even if you can't find it at this moment. Shall we take your car to the hospital or get a taxi?"

> " *consider hospitalization or legal commitment* "

If necessary, consider hospitalization or legal commitment. Most industrial nations have facilities for the assessment, care, and treatment of persons at risk of suicide. Hospital mental health or psychiatric units are acceptable, safe places for persons at risk. Laws and regulations permit the involuntary holding of persons at risk who are a danger to themselves and won't agree voluntarily to preventative measures. Most emergency service providers (911, paramedics, police services, crisis lines) are aware of and can put you in contact with the resources in your community who are responsible for enforcing these laws.

There are two objectives for this task:

1) develop a mutual understanding of the factors that increase risk;
2) show that you take the issue of suicide seriously by being thorough in your risk review.

Task 5: Contract a Safeplan

CONTRACT

This task involves you and the person at risk agreeing to a plan that prevents the immediate risk of suicide. What goes into the safeplan was discussed in some detail in chapter three. In this chapter, we focus on the caregiver and person at risk process that makes a safeplan safe. That process is contracting. The aim of contracting is an agreement that includes a number of commitments.

Principles of a good safeplan

While the risk review and safeplan protectors give detail to a particular safeplan, there are several principles of any good safeplan.

1. **Freedom to Think about Suicide**. In any safeplan, there must be freedom to continue thinking about and discussing the option of suicide. It is unrealistic to expect so much change from the intervention that the person at risk no longer has thoughts of suicide. The change you are looking for is their promise not to act upon those thoughts of suicide during the period of time specified in the safeplan.

2. **Specificity**. Details about the things to be done and who will do them must be clearly understood. Plans should always be specific. Vague and nonspecific plans can be dangerous.

3. **Limited Objectives**. Remember that your job is to intervene until the immediate danger or threat of suicide has passed or until additional assistance and resources can be accessed. The safeplan is not meant to be a total solution for all the person's problems. It is fine if the safeplan makes a start on solving some of the problems, but the main purpose is to create a "safety space" — an amount of time that is safe from suicide. Be realistic. A commitment for one week, one day or one hour is much better than an unrealistic commitment.

4. **Real Agreement**. Ask the person to repeat the safeplan and the commitments that flow from it. As the person says these words out loud, both you and they will experience a feeling of relief. The person at risk should be able to describe the safeplan with sincerity and a sense of ownership. If they can't, there may be parts of the safeplan that need to be adjusted.

5. **Crisis Support**. Confirm some arrangement for emergency support if the steps of your safeplan cannot be carried out or if the commitments cannot be maintained. Talk to the formal and informal resources that may form part of a supportive "safety net" and get their permission to be involved. If appropriate, have the person at risk rehearse contacting and using the resources that will serve as crisis supports. Encourage people to write key details (such as crisis line numbers) down. People in crisis can easily forget details.

6. **Suicide-Safe the Environment**. Well-intentioned agreements not to harm oneself are sometimes difficult to keep. When a person at risk's plan includes a chosen means of harm, the means should be removed. While particularly important in higher risk situations, it is a good idea to remove other dangerous items from the environment even when these items are not a part of the person at risk's plan for suicide. For example, it might be possible to lock up firearms, drugs and medicines. Most law enforcement agencies will hold surrendered firearms. Prescribed medications should be continued but someone could help dispense them on an as-needed basis. Dated or discontinued medications should be returned to a pharmacy for disposal. If you are unsure about medications, check with the practitioner who prescribed them. Alcohol and illegal drug intake should be discouraged since these substances may depress the person at risk or stimulate them to act impulsively.

The following example illustrates one way in which you might test to see if an agreement exists:

> I can understand that things seem terrible to you and that it seems like the pain won't ever stop. But help is available and people do get through it. It'll take some work on your part, but it can happen. I want your agreement that you will keep yourself safe from suicide between now and when we get together tomorrow at noon. If thoughts of suicide really build up, I still want your promise to do nothing until you talk to me or to the crisis line that you just talked to. If there should be some delay in contacting me, you are promising to call the crisis line. We are agreeing that you will hand over the pills you have except some that you need to take until we meet. We are also agreeing to go to the counselor's office tomorrow at 2:00 PM. Okay, have I said the things that we have agreed on? Can you repeat our agreement in your own words to see what it feels like?

There are two objectives for this task:

1) to contract a safeplan,
2) to provide a sense of hope.

Task 6: Follow-up on Commitments

The previous task is finished when you and the person at risk agree to the safeplan. Your last task is to follow-up on all the commitments in the safeplan to see that they are done.

FOLLOW-UP   You need to follow-up with any resources that you linked to as a part of the safeplan. The more formal the resource, the more likely you will need to establish how you can follow-up at the time you create and agree to the safeplan. For example, you might say to a health worker, "Can I phone you to make sure they keep their appointment with you and to basically know that everything went okay?" Doing this step at the time of contracting with the person at risk present, makes it clear to the health worker that the person at risk is giving you permission to make this inquiry. You may need to get written permission from the person at risk as well. Check with the resource you are referring to.

Commitments you made should be kept since failing to do so will be experienced as a loss by the person at risk. Only make commitments that you can and want to complete. Don't try to do too much. The person at risk should feel as if they are doing as much as they can to minimize the danger. If you try to be too helpful, the person at risk may feel that you are not respecting their desire to live. If you try to do more than you want to do or feel comfortable doing, the resentment or anxiety you will experience will eventually be apparent to the person at risk. Be honest with yourself and with them from the very beginning. Do not be afraid to offer new information about your feelings and capabilities as you discover them.

Accomplishing these six tasks may resolve the issue of suicide altogether. At the very least, accomplishing the tasks provides practical ways to stay safe until problems and painful concerns can be addressed, making it more likely that thoughts of suicide will eventually end. The person at risk has been able to make use of you as a support or resource at a time when they were feeling overwhelmed. Your involvement is clear evidence that they are not alone.

And you are not alone either. There are many other resources that can be involved in helping to prevent a suicide. As noted in chapter three, some contact with these resources ought to be included in the agreement that you negotiate. This may involve bringing in friends

assisting

or relatives to help or referring the person to other resources for assistance.

For yourself, you may want to include consultation with your supervisor, contact with a mental health professional, or sharing with a trusted colleague. These people can support your agreement and may offer other suggestions or plans to further your work with the person at risk.

There are two objectives for this task:

1) to ensure that commitments are kept,
2) to provide a sense of safety.

Suicide First-Aid Situations

The following examples demonstrate how these six tasks might unfold in actual situations.

Keeping Your Goal in Focus

You are a physical education teacher. One of your students, Jan, is normally a happy, active participant in gym class. Today she seems unusually withdrawn and sad. You take her aside to try to **explore** what these changes might mean. Are they *invitations* to help?

YOU:　*Jan, you haven't seemed to be yourself lately. What's been happening to you?*

JAN:　*Nothing! I'm just tired.*

Jan is not eager to talk, but you continue to **explore** for the meaning of these invitations.

YOU:　*Something seems to be on your mind. Want to talk about it?*

JAN:　*Not really. I said I'm just tired. That's all.*

YOU:　*Being tired is sometimes connected to feeling sad or something that wears you out.*

She doesn't answer, but you notice that she looks down and chews her lip. You realize that invitations are being offered right in this conversation. She is showing you that something is bothering her. You continue with patience and persistence.

YOU: *I wanted to let you know that I do see that something is bothering you.*

JAN: *I'm pregnant.*

Jan begins to cry as she blurts out her answer. You are supportive and continue your efforts to connect with her.

YOU: *That must be pretty scary for you.*

JAN: *Yeah, and I don't know what to do. My father will be furious at me.*

YOU: *You're worried that your dad will be angry with you?*

JAN: *More than that, he'll be ashamed of me. He doesn't think you should have sex until you're married — especially if you're a girl.*

You have succeeded in earning some of Jan's trust. You have discovered two stressful events, her pregnancy and her belief that her father will be very disappointed. You continue to **explore** what all of this means to her.

YOU: *I'd like to help. Let's talk more. Tell me more about how you are feeling.*

JAN: *I'm angry and afraid. At the same time, it makes me feel... I don't know... grown up, I guess, and I like that. I'm so confused.*

YOU: *Confused?*

JAN: *Yes, about myself... my feelings... and Kurt...*

YOU: *Kurt's your boyfriend, right?*

JAN: *Yes, but he won't care. He'll just want me to get rid of it.*

YOU: *How does that make you feel?*

JAN: *Like I'm all alone. Nobody cares whether I live or die.*

This last mysterious comment triggers a gut feeling in you. You recall other teenagers you've known who have felt life wasn't worth living when they thought they had failed their parents. Now she is offering *invitations* that could easily be connected to suicide. You take a chance that something similar is going on with Jan and decide to specifically **ask** about thoughts of suicide.

YOU: *I care whether you live or die. Are you thinking about dying?... about killing yourself?*

JAN: *Yeah. The thought has crossed my mind, more than once.*

There it is — she has decided to be open and to take a chance on you. The two of you are now connected in a situation that calls for a suicide intervention. You want to make it clear that you understand that.

YOU: *All of this has got you thinking about suicide?*

JAN: *Yes.*

You now know that the things she told you about are related to wanting to die. You know she needs to talk about that and you need to **listen**.

YOU: *So suicide and your father's reaction are connected? What do you think your father will do when he finds out?*

JAN: *He'll get angry and tell me how disappointed he feels. He expects so much of me... I don't know if I can handle his disappointment. That is when I think about killing myself. I just cannot see a way past telling him.*

YOU: *What about your mother?*

JAN: *She can't stop him... Oh, she'll cry and comfort me and then blame herself for not bringing me up right.*

To see if there is a shared understanding of what you've learned to this point, you rephrase what you have heard.

YOU: *So suicide comes to your mind because you think you have really disappointed your parents by getting pregnant.*

JAN: *That's about it.*

You know the reasons for dying and they seem to tell what some the reasons for living might be. You try to see if you have heard them correctly.

YOU: *Would you like to get through this tough time with your parents...?*

JAN: *Second chances don't come easy in our family. I just don't know what to do... have the baby... but how to care for it?*

YOU: *So you would like a second chance, but what to do is your biggest problem right now?*

JAN: *Yeah, but I can never think straight when I am in a jam... if only I hadn't been so stupid...*

YOU: *Are you thinking about an abortion?*

JAN: *I don't think so. That doesn't feel right to me.*

YOU: *Are you thinking about adoption?*

JAN: *No way. I'm not going to go through all the trouble of giving birth just to give away the baby.*

YOU: *What else have you considered?*

JAN: *My friends think I should run away.*

YOU: *Is that what you really want to do?*

JAN: *No. I don't want to be on my own yet. I like it at home. But I don't want to hurt my folks. And I don't want to have them down on me for the rest of my life.*

YOU: *So, you actually have some ideas about what you want, but you are not sure you have any hope of getting them to happen basically because of your parents. Would you like to find a way to see if your parents could come through for you?*

JAN: *Yes, I would.*

There are reasons for living and you have some ideas about what a *safeplan* might include. You need to **review** the risk to see what else might be needed in the *safeplan*.

YOU: *So, to have a chance to work things out with your parents, we need to protect against suicide. Let's review the risk of suicide so we can find ways to protect against it. Have you thought about how you would kill yourself?*

JAN: *Not really.*

YOU: *Have you ever tried to hurt yourself before?*

JAN: *No.*

YOU: *When you think about facing your parents, do you feel pain that you just can't stand?*

JAN: *Not really; I just go do something else for a while. I am really not as troubled as I seem all the time. The truth is I just hoped you would notice me.*

YOU: *Are you receiving or have you ever received mental health care?*

JAN: *Why are you asking that?*

YOU: *Because people who are or have been are often at greater risk of suicide and may need help from a health worker.*

JAN: *Oh, no I never have.*

YOU: *So, I guess us being connected is helping you feel less alone. Are their other people you can count on?*

JAN: *My friends help but they can't help with the main thing which is dealing with my parents. I now see that that is what I hope you can help with.*

The primary risk alert is her thoughts of suicide. Although she may think she does not know what to do and can't think under pressure, she is actually doing quite well in this intervention. The main thing is to find someone to help her talk with her parents. You do not feel qualified to do that but the counselor will. You decide to see if you and she have the same understanding.

YOU: *Things are getting clearer as we talk but you still don't know how to talk with your parents. That is the primary danger. My idea is that you need someone who can be a go-between for you and your parents — someone who can slow the discussion down and keep it respectful.*

JAN: *Yeah.*

YOU: *What if we got Mr. Kramer, the school counselor, involved and then figured a way to call your folks in? I don't feel like I know enough about those kinds of situations to do as well by you as he can. He deals with things like this all the time.*

JAN: *Yeah, I would be willing to see what he is like. I don't know anything about him except the general word around the school, which is good.*

There are a few additional things that you need in the *safeplan* and then you will see if the two of can agree on the plan.

YOU: *I will contact him today and set up an appointment. You come by after school and I will let you know what I have found out. In the meantime, could you promise me that you won't do anything to hurt yourself until then and if suicide thoughts should build up that you will come and see me even if I am in class or on a break? I know you are saying that suicide is not likely but let's just be really safe and agree to all of this. Is that okay? Can you repeat it back to me?*

JAN: *You have my word. I will see you at the end of the day. I will see you no matter what if I can't keep my promise about suicide. At the end of the day, we will see where we are with Mr. Kramer.*

YOU: *'Great. If I find out anything sooner, I may come and get you. I assume you want me to come with you to see Mr. Kramer?*

JAN: *Yes. Thank you.*

You **follow-up** on your *commitments* to the safeplan by contacting Mr. Kramer. You review the risk and the current safeplan with him and find out when an appointment is possible. Depending upon the time frame for the transfer of care to be accomplished, you may need additional resources for the period of time in between but it is likely that Mr. Kramer will see her today and he can make the next intervention.

Jan was looking for help in dealing with a stress that had overwhelmed her. She did not want to end her life but was beginning to view suicide as the only choice available to her. By actively listening to her reasons for dying, you gained her trust. Then Jan was able to look for reasons for living. The problems are not solved yet, but she is safe while other supports are being put in place.

All in a Day's Work

You are a veteran police officer. You and your partner are patrolling your district when you come upon a small crowd looking up at the top of a multistory building. You discover that there is a young man standing on the ledge of that building. Your partner calls for backup and moves the crowd back across the street while you gain access to the roof. As you get close to the young man, he starts by warning you to stay back.

HIM: *Stay where you are!*

YOU: *I hear you, and I'm not coming any closer. If you are not quite sure what you want to do, I want to give you lots time — and space.*

A long silence ensues. You decide to try another approach, but are interrupted.

HIM: *That's right. Can't jump and can't get down.*

Almost certainly this is an *invitation* to help with suicide. Just to make sure, you **ask** directly about suicide.

YOU: *Can't commit suicide but can't give up the option either?*

HIM: *Exactly.*

Suicide is out in the open very quickly. Now we need to find out what the *reasons for dying and living* are.

YOU: *Tell me about the "can't get down" part.*

HIM: *I can't tell you about it. That's how bad it is.*

YOU: *Something you can't tell me about because of this uniform, or plain can't tell anyone about?*

HIM: *Perhaps you more so, but I can't tell anyone.*

YOU: *Something that happened just lately?*

HIM: *I've known for a while I guess, but now I really know.*

It must be some kind of taboo topic with all of the pain he shows when he gets close to just the thought of talking about it. He knows what it is, of course. It is not necessary that you know specifically. You do know that it has him thinking about suicide.

YOU: *So dealing with whatever this thing "that is really hard to talk about," is stopping you from coming down.*

HIM: *Exactly. It got me up here and it won't let me come down.*

You decide that you know enough about the reasons for dying for now. You turn to **listening** for the *reasons for living*.

YOU: *And something is stopping you from jumping?*

HIM: *It is a hell of lot harder to do this than I thought it would be. I got up here to fix myself once and for all, and now...*

YOU: *So you are kinda stuck. Don't want to jump, but can't come down.*

There is clearly a part that doesn't want to die. You wonder if you can name the hope — help make the *reason for living* more obvious.

YOU: *Would you like to hope that you could talk about this hard to talk about thing with someone?*

HIM: *Are you going to arrest me?*

So he needs to know what might happen in the *safeplan* before he can agree to it. You know that he has thoughts of suicide and a plan to carry it out. You have seen the mental pain. You don't need to **review** anything else about the *risk* at this moment unless something comes up. You can't disable his suicide plan without his help and that is the most immediate concern. And he needs information before he can cooperate with you. You need to start the process of **contracting** to find out what kind of *safeplan* he can *commit* to.

YOU: *No, but you need to meet with members of our Community Response Team. They might want you to go to the hospital so you can be in a safe place. They are close by and are the kind of people who will listen to what you are trying to deal with — this stuff that is so hard to talk about.*

HIM: *I am stuck, stuck, stuck.*

YOU: *So there is a part that would like to talk to someone, but the first step seems impossible.*

HIM: *You got it!*

He didn't reject those *safeplan* ideas, but he needs some other steps in between.

YOU: *I hear you. Could you tell me your name?*

HIM: *George.*

That was one step. You will try for another.

YOU: *George, do you think you could maybe sit down? You might feel a little less stuck that way.*

GEORGE: *I guess so but only if you promise not to move.*

YOU: *Okay, but once you're sitting down, can you promise not to move either?*

GEORGE: *Okay.*

He sits down. That was another, bigger step. Now to find out what the next step needs to be.

YOU: *Now George, what do you suppose we need to do next. Do you think we should try to find a way to talk about this thing now? That might be a start at finding out that it is possible. Or, do you think we should find a way to get you in touch with the Resource Team and figure out the rest from there?*

GEORGE: *The Resource Team, I guess. Are you going to handcuff me?*

YOU: *Yes, but only until we get to the Response Team. I have arranged a way out the back of the building so no one recognizes you. Will that be okay?*

GEORGE: *Okay.*

Both of you **follow-up** on your *commitments* in the *safeplan*. On the way down, George tells you that last night he had his first homo-

assisting

sexual experience. You get his permission to tell the Response Team about this so that he has a place to start in talking about this issue.

This is a situation in which a caregiver can feel powerless or over-whelmed and become paralyzed. This officer drew upon her knowledge of the tasks to overcome any feelings that might have paralyzed her. While seeming to move through the tasks very quickly in this situation, that is just how fast she was able to go with this young man. It won't always go this quickly. Every situation is different. The usefulness of the tasks, however, remains constant.

Patience, When You Need it Most

You are a physician who works two days a week at an Indian Affairs med-center. This morning you put a cast on the arm of a 38 year-old woman and stitched a gash in her forehead. She was injured in what the police described as a suspicious, single-vehicle car accident. Her car struck an abutment on a clear stretch of road at high speed and with no apparent application of brakes. She had not been drinking. She was fortunate to come out of the crash with only minor injuries. The police have told you that there have been two suicides in her immediate family, and four more on the reserve in the past six months.

You have asked her about the accident. She says she doesn't know how it happened. She is staring at the floor. Her injuries do not require hospitalization and you are tempted to just let her go home. Yet your concern leads you to try to **explore** further to see if these actions are *invitations*. You sit down on a stool in the treatment room. She is sitting on the table.

YOU: *That's it for the cast and stitches Sarah. How do you feel?*

SARAH: *I'm okay.*

YOU: *You will likely have some pain around the cut when the freezing comes out. And I suspect your arm is hurting now, am I right?*

SARAH: *Some.*

YOU: *I can give you something for the pain. Are you on any medication now?*

SARAH: *No.*

YOU: *I don't want you drinking with the medication. All right?*

She barely nods. This isn't going to be easy. You knew that talking with her would likely be difficult. You are treated with respect by the patients, but they do not talk much with you. Sometimes the cultural gulf feels very wide. Yet sometimes it is bridged and connections are made. You don't like how your comment about drinking might have sounded.

YOU: *I'm sorry about the way I said that. I just meant that drinking interferes with the value of the drug.*

SARAH: *I don't drink.*

YOU: *No?*

SARAH: *No.*

YOU: *That's good.*

As the silence lays heavily between you, you are again tempted to end the conversation. Her eyes do not meet yours, but you are used to that. You give her the same respect by looking down at the floor as well, and relaxing. You decide to ask the obvious — to **ask** about the possibility of *suicide*.

YOU: *Sarah, let me be honest. I'm concerned about you. The accident you had today worries me.*

You look up. Sarah doesn't respond.

YOU: *I know in your culture, asking about personal things is sometimes seen as interfering in someone's life, as not respecting or caring for someone. In my culture these things are difficult to talk about as well, but not asking is seen as not caring. I am concerned, Sarah, about the suicides here. I know they've touched you as well. In my experience, when people feel really low they sometimes think of suicide. Is that happening for you?*

You want to keep looking up, but you force yourself to return your gaze to the floor.

SARAH: *Maybe. It's not something we talk about in my family.*

YOU: *Because of what's happened?*

SARAH: *My brother and my uncle died that way. They never left any message.*

YOU: *You didn't see anything coming?*

SARAH: *My brother was on drugs; my uncle drank too much. I knew that.*

YOU: *But you didn't know what was wrong, or you didn't want to interfere?*

SARAH: *I didn't know what to say, though I did try to talk to my brother. It didn't do any good.*

You feel somewhat connected at this point but want to shift the focus back to Sarah and her feelings and behavior.

YOU: *But you tried. I think we have to try. Sarah, are you feeling like you want to die as well?*

Sarah doesn't say anything, but she nods.

YOU: *Is that what the accident today is about?*

SARAH: *I don't want to say. I don't want anybody to know.*

YOU: *Are you planning on trying again?*

She doesn't answer.

YOU: *Are you still thinking about taking your life Sarah?*

SARAH: *I don't know.*

You are uncertain about whether this indicates some **ambivalence** on her part, or whether she is putting you off. You try speaking speaking for the part that wants to live.

YOU: *It sounds to me like life is very painful for you right now. Would you like to get through this pain to something better?*

SARAH: *I don't know. Things don't work out.*

YOU: *But would you like them to work out?*

She shrugs, and winces at the pain in her arm as she does so. You decide to use this in a way that has worked with others.

YOU: *Sarah, the pain that you feel in life is something like what's happening in your arm. Your arm hurts. If it isn't dealt with, the pain becomes so intense that we can't stand it and will do most anything to make it stop. I can help stop the pain in your arm, or at least make it manageable while your body heals it. Life pain can also be dealt with. Yes it's hard, and you don't know what to do, but it can change. Would you like to try?*

SARAH: *I guess. I need time to think. Do I have to stay here?*

YOU: *Can you tell me more about your life pain?*

SARAH: *Not now. Do I have to stay here?*

YOU: *What has been happening for you lately?*

SARAH: *Nothing. Do I have to stay here?*

You don't know anything more about the reasons for dying except that they exist. You are not even sure if it is what is making Sarah want to leave. You could have her conveyed to a city hospital, but you don't think that would be helpful. There are mental health workers on the reserve who would be useful. And there may be other resources, including family members, on the reserve that could be helpful. You want to develop some type of safeplan using supports that are familiar for her if you can.

YOU: *No you don't. But I want us to agree that you need time to think and maybe somebody to help with the life pain. Sarah, is there anyone you can talk to?*

SARAH: *No one knows.*

YOU: *Sarah, I can have some people here see you. There are some workers who would talk with you.*

SARAH: *Then everyone would know. Everybody knows what happens here.*

YOU: *Then I could have someone see you in the city.*

SARAH: *They would still know.*

YOU: *I think we could find a way that they wouldn't. Is there anyone else here in the community that you might talk with, who would be helpful to you? Like an elder?*

SARAH: *I don't want to disappoint elders.*

YOU: *Sometimes we disappoint our elders by not talking to them. Do you have someone in mind?*

SARAH: *Maybe. I need to think. Can I go now?*

YOU: *Where will you go?*

SARAH: *Home.*

YOU: *Do you live alone?*

SARAH: *No, I live with my sister and her family. She is in the waiting room now and she'll be wondering what is taking so long.*

You now realize part of the reason why she is in such a hurry to leave: staying longer and talking is the same to her as admitting her thoughts of suicide to the world. You want to make sure you have heard both the *reasons for dying and for living*.

YOU: *You are torn. The most immediate worry is that you don't want anyone to know that you are thinking about suicide but there is a part that wants to get this out in the open a* *bit so you will have time to think. It may be that the side that wants you to keep quiet is also the side that wants to commit suicide. The side that wants you to live wants you to get help.*

SARAH: *Yes, I suppose all of that is true but I need something in the middle right now.*

That is the first thing she has contributed on her own. You need to find a safeplan that will give her the time to do some more thinking. Maybe you can get her to share these thoughts with her sister as part of that plan.

YOU: *I realize you need some time but I would like you to agree to keep yourself safe until we can talk again when I'm back on Thursday. And I will give you my number in the city if you need to talk with me in the meantime. And most important I think is to involve some one else, some one like your sister. Can we trust her to help us Sarah?*

SARAH: *Yes, I suppose I can go that far.*

YOU: *I'd like to ask her in so we can speak with her together. I want us to tell her that you are hurting physically and inside with thoughts of suicide, and that you need special care right now. I want her to know exactly what you and I have planned and why. Is that okay?*

She nods. You want more confirmation that she agrees with the *safeplan*.

YOU: *What are we agreeing to?*

SARAH: *I'll see you Thursday.*

YOU: *And?*

SARAH: *And you give me your number and I won't do anything.*

YOU: *Do anything?*

SARAH: *Anything to harm myself — and my sister is going to know all of this.*

You start **following-up** by asking her sister to come into the room. You will tell her what is happening and enlist her support. You will also provide her and Sarah with your number and set time aside to see her on your next visit. You plan to revisit the suicide intervention tasks at that time and see if you can help Sarah decide about additional resources.

Patience and flexibility, along with persistence, are the hallmarks of suicide intervention. In this situation, making a connection took a long time. Sarah set the speed or pace of the intervention and the caregiver was sensitive to this throughout. Sarah was more concerned about shame or embarrassment. The caregiver kept her focus on preventing the immediate risk of suicide. Although Sarah wanted help, the help had to be organized into small steps that she could handle.

Preventive Action Plan

You are a youth worker attached to a vocational school for younger adults who previously dropped out of high school. One of the students, Barb, seems to be looking aimlessly at pamphlets in the outer office. You decide to invite her into your office. Almost immediately she reveals that she has just been diagnosed with a mental disorder, a depression. You see this an *invitation* to connect with her.

YOU: *What makes you think that?*

BARB: *That is what the shrink said. I have to start taking these pills.*

YOU: *And, the depression has got you depressed?*

BARB: *Angry is more like it. Wouldn't you be too?*

You respond in a way that stays focused on her feelings and encourages her to open up a bit more with you.

YOU: *This is hitting you pretty hard.*

BARB: *Yes! And I want to hit back.*

YOU: *Maybe the medication will work.*

BARB: *Not with my luck. Besides when you have depression at my age, you are in for a life of trouble. What's the use!*

She doesn't want to be encouraged. You decide to find out if these indirect statements are actually *invitations* to help with suicide. You decide to **ask** directly about her intentions.

YOU: *"What's the use" might be a way of saying that you are thinking about suicide. Are you thinking about suicide?*

BARB: *No. I thought about it for a second but that's all. I need a place to stay.*

YOU: *Then you are not now thinking about suicide?*

BARB: *No. I told you. I learned my lesson about that before.*

YOU: *What lesson?*

BARB: *I tried once before, but was that ever a mistake!*

YOU: *In what way?*

BARB: *One moment I was feeling bad and next I was shoving pills down my throat. But I was stupid. My mother found out and took me to the hospital. Everyone there seemed to think I was just trying to get something and then nobody ever talked about it again. Nothing changed. Look, I need to find a place to stay.*

She is saying she is not currently thinking about suicide. She also seems to regard her earlier suicidal behavior as having a protective effect. Much more likely, it doesn't. You also worry about the impulsiveness of her previous attempt. You have gathered some *risk* **review** information. You decide to complete that process to gauge the possibility of current or future suicidal behavior.

YOU: *When you thought about suicide, did you think about how you would do it?*

BARB: *No. I told you. It just went through my head. I need to find a place to stay.*

This goes along with her belief that she is not considering suicide as an option but you want more information. This "needing a place to stay" thing has been said twice. It might imply something about resources and/or other stresses.

YOU: *Why are you needing a place to stay?*

BARB: *I need some time to figure out what to do with mom. She will know that something is bothering me. She will get it out of me and then she will get so upset. She has enough on her plate just keeping us fed and clothed.*

YOU: *Wouldn't it be good to have her support?*

BARB: *Yes, but....*

YOU: *So it feels like you are alone with this? The shrink doesn't count in the alone part?*

BARB: *No, I just met her. Mom is the problem. She didn't know what to do after what happened at the hospital last time. She got so upset. She cried a lot. She hid it, but I knew she was disappointed in me — or something like that.*

YOU: *Yes, but this time you already have help.*

BARB: *Yes, but this time I know it's depression.*

She has prior suicidal behavior. She feels like she is without resources. The relationship with the psychiatrist is new and undeveloped. On the other hand, it seems clear that if a connection could be renewed with her mother, she would feel supported. While she doesn't have thoughts of suicide now there is a real danger that she could in the near future as she struggles to learn how to cope with depression. On the other hand, she keeps telling you that she wants to live. You decide to see if you can get her to **contract** a *safeplan* that will keep her safe.

YOU: *Now, I know you aren't thinking about suicide now and hopefully you won't, just like you are trying to tell me. But you know how you said that once before you were just feeling bad and the next thing you knew...*

BARB: *Yes.*

YOU: *Well, can we make some agreement about that, just in case, before we get back to what to do about mom?*

BARB: *What do you mean?*

YOU: *Let's say that you would promise to tell someone that you were having thoughts of suicide, if you did, before you did anything to harm yourself.*

BARB: *Tell who?*

YOU: *Well, you could tell me.*

BARB: *Sure. And I don't mean it like that. If somebody had just talked about depression and suicide the first time I would have gotten help with this back then and that part would be done already.*

YOU: *We will need to let your shrink know about this too.*

BARB: *I suppose she would want to know.*

You have an agreement on part of what you need but there are several more things that need doing before you have a complete *safeplan*. The most immediate is to try to renew the connection between Barb and her mother.

YOU: *So, you would really like to have your mother's support, but you are not sure how she will react when you tell her about your diagnosis?*

BARB: *Yes. She just got so upset last time I was this depressed and she didn't even know what was going on.*

YOU: *I get the sense that most of the time you have a close relationship with your mom, but that depression has separated the two of you once before and you are worried that it will do it again. Is this close?*

BARB: *Yes.*

YOU:	*If you want, maybe I or your shrink can help you talk to your mom? There wouldn't be any guarantee, of course, but it seems like having your mom understand is important and more than worth a try.*
BARB:	*I guess I have to tell her something.*
YOU:	*Me or your shrink?*
BARB:	*You or maybe both, if you can arrange it. It is hard to get in to see her.*
YOU:	*Okay, let me check on that first and then we will know exactly what we agreed to do.*

You will add details to the safeplan once you know what the Doctor says. Assuming the Doctor wants to help and can do so fairly soon, you will want to make sure you can **follow-up** the *safeplan* with the Doctor if she is taking over from here.

At this moment, you are more concerned about suicide than Barb is. Putting a "preventive" *safeplan* into place allows her the opportunity to explore coping strategies with important supports in place. Many suicide first-aid interventions are like this. Suicide is acknowledged and averted well before it becomes likely to occur.

Ready, Willing and Able

You are a sergeant in the army. You are on peacekeeping duty in foreign country. Part of your training has included the *ASIST* workshop. You carry your intervention model and review card with you at all times.

It is mail time. Your squad is sitting in the mess tent reading their mail. You are not sure why you look up but you do. You see that corporal Smith has just gone pale as a ghost and then has quickly hidden his reaction. You ask corporal Smith to remain behind as others move back to the hut. Something in the mail knocked the life out of him. You want to know what it is and what it means. You know that he saw you notice his reaction. He is *inviting* you to **explore** what that "look" meant.

YOU:	*Some bad news?*
SMITH:	*I'm okay. Gee, you watch over us like a mother hen.*
YOU:	*It's part of my job. I am guessing, maybe a "Dear John" letter. If it was a death or something the army usually helps with, I would have known first.*

SMITH:	*You are pretty sharp Sarge but I have been expecting it. No sweat.*
YOU:	*Your reaction was not, "no sweat." What I saw scared me and it may have scared you too.*
SMITH:	*At first it did and then I just thought, "that clinches it."*
YOU:	*That clinches it?*
SMITH:	*The last straw.*
YOU:	*The last straw for the relationship?*
SMITH:	*No, last straw... for everything.*

He keeps sending *invitations* that are more and more likely to be related to *suicide*. It is time to **ask** directly.

YOU:	*So it is suicide you are talking about?*
SMITH:	*Yep. There is pin in a grenade with my name on it.*
YOU:	*Going there now?*
SMITH:	*I was thinking about it. What better sign could I get.*

He knows what is going to happen now that he told me this so there is no need to rush into anything. It is much better to see how much he can be involved in the process. You pull out your card. You know, without looking, that you need to **listen** to the *reasons for dying and living*.

YOU:	*This card reminds me of what I need to do about suicide. I might want to refer to it. You are free to look at it too, if you want. There are no secrets here. Is that okay?*
SMITH:	*Sure, whatever you want.*
YOU:	*When you say "last straw" it means things were bothering you before you got the Dear John letter?*
SMITH:	*I was just barely hanging on here. Waiting for my time to be up and then word of the extension came. She was the only thing keeping me going. We didn't have time to develop a really solid relationship before I was sent here but still she was all that was keeping me going.*
YOU:	*You sure hid that well or I wasn't looking. I guess it means you have been thinking about suicide a lot?*
SMITH:	*Every day since the extension came down. Several times I almost pulled the pin. But you wouldn't have seen it coming. I wasn't letting anyone see. I did not want to let anyone down. I did not want anyone to think I could not*

pull my share. Best to get it over with all at once and get a replacement.

It shocks you to think you didn't see it before but that was then and now is now. Come to think about it, why now?

YOU: *It seems like the closer suicide gets, the more some part of you says, "wait a minute." After all you let me see that something was bothering you this time and you are talking to me.*

SMITH: *Something. I don't have that anger right now. When I read the letter, it just took the last spark out of me. Now I feel numb almost.*

YOU: *It felt like there are lots of reasons for dying but there is something that is stopping you for now.*

SMITH: *Yes, but more like the lack of something is stopping me.*

YOU: *Maybe some part of you made you numb to protect you from suicide?*

SMITH: *Strange isn't it.*

YOU: *We don't know what it is but you will have to stay alive to have a chance to find out what it is.*

SMITH: *I guess so.*

You know, without looking at the card, that you are ready to move on to **reviewing** the *risk*.

YOU: *Now I want to find out more about the risk so that we will have time to find out more about what might keep you alive. The medical people are going to want to know about the risk too.*

You knew how, and more or less when, you would kill yourself. You felt pain that was close to being unbearable at times. You were certainly feeling alone with this and now way more so. Have you ever attempted suicide before?

SMITH: *No.*

YOU: *Ever been treated for a mental health concern?*

SMITH: *No, until now I guess.*

YOU: *Suicide is not a mental health concern. It is something people sometimes think about for many different reasons. An underlying mental health concern could be part of suicide but it might not be.*

You take a quick look at your prompter card.

YOU: *That is all on risk. How does it sound to you.*

SMITH: *Like I am either very lucky or very stupid to be talking to you about this. Can't say which yet.*

YOU: *I understand that.*

It is time for the *safeplan*. The protocol for the *safeplan* is pretty clear. There is too much immediate danger for anything else. There is no shortage of ways to kill yourself here.

YOU: *So I guess we should go over to see the doc now. I will, of course, go with you. I need to let the captain know what is going on but he knows how this works too. Are you ready?*

SMITH: *Yes, I guess so. Should I get my stuff?*

YOU: *No, lets go see what they say first.*

SMITH: *Okay and, sarge, thanks, I hope.*

You put your card away and the two of you start **following-up** on your *commitments*. You know that you might need your card again when you share your *risk* **review** and *safeplan* with the medical people.

This caregiver was ready, willing and able to help. His intervention card was a symbol for and a reminder of what he knew how to do.

When You Least Expect It

Jim is a coworker whom you have known for a long time. At one time your families socialized together, but Jim and his wife have been having some difficulties and social contact has stopped. Jim has been very quiet at work lately. Business is very slow and the staff is afraid of layoffs. You and Jim are having a drink after work and discussing the latest rumors of company downsizing. He has downed two drinks to your one and is ordering another round.

You're concerned how much and how fast he is drinking.

YOU: *Whoa, I'm not ready for another one yet. You're getting way ahead of me. Is this layoff thing bothering you that much?*

JIM: *What, you think I'm drinking because of all the rumbles at work?*

YOU: *Well, I'm wondering. I'm sure sick of worrying about it.*

JIM: *I'm not. They'll do whatever they're going to do. We can't do anything about it.*

YOU: *Well it scares me. I don't know what I'd do for another job with the way things are in our field.*

JIM: *You'd find something.*

YOU: *What about you?*

JIM: *You mean what about a man in his fifties? Down the tubes, I guess. Who cares?*

Jim is speaking very quietly. His face appears sad. He stares at the drink in his hand, only looking up when the waiter approaches with the fresh round.

YOU: *Well, we all do.*

JIM: *It doesn't matter to me.*

YOU: *You've got to be kidding. Of course it does!*

JIM: *No, it doesn't. I'm telling you I don't feel anything about it. I don't feel anything about anything. Anyway, let's drop it.*

Your concern is increasing. You don't want to drop it. You want to **explore** the hidden but not so hidden meanings in the things he is saying.

YOU: *Jim, you look really sad.*

JIM: *Yeah, well it's all right.*

There is a catch in his voice as he says this and he looks away. He could easily make you believe everything is okay but he is not doing that. He is clearly *inviting* you to **explore** further.

YOU: *What is it Jim? Is it the job, your wife? What's bothering you?*

JIM: *It's me. I don't feel much of anything. I haven't for a long time. Pearl couldn't take it anymore. I don't blame her.*

YOU: *Take what?*

JIM: *My depression. I've been depressed for years.*

YOU: *Have you seen anyone, gotten some help?*

JIM: *Yeah, I saw a psychiatrist when I was in the northern office two years ago. She gave me pills, lots of pills. She was nice but it didn't help. I'm hell to live with, because*

I don't care. Pearl couldn't stand it. Nobody can. It isn't going to change.

You have learned a lot about troubles in Jim's life. He is willing to talk to you. You are engaged in serious conversation. While he says he doesn't care, you notice that there are tears in his eyes as he finishes his drink and signals for another. You decide to take it a step further and **ask** if *suicide* is a possibility.

YOU: *Jim, this sounds really bad. I had no idea. Let me ask you something. Have you considered, or are you considering suicide? Is that why you say it doesn't matter?*

JIM: *Yes. It would be such a blessing just to leave it all behind. When you are depressed, I mean really depressed, life is a sham.*

YOU: *You make it sound so final!*

JIM: *It is.*

You think you have heard the *reasons for dying*. You decide to check if you have been **listening** by reflecting back what you have heard.

YOU: *So basically this depression has got you to the point where everything is headed toward suicide. It's just a matter of time?*

JIM: *Yes, but I need to get it done and quit thinking about it.*

You think you just heard a *reason for living*. You decide to make sure you have been **listening** by reflecting back what you have heard.

YOU: *Some part is not quite sure?*

JIM: *I can't imagine what part that could be.*

There is at least a small part that is unsure. There is some ambivalence. You decide to move on to **review** the *risk*. More ambivalence might surface from that or at least you will have a clearer idea of the danger.

YOU: *Have you thought of how you'd do it?*

JIM: *The place I am living now is on the eleventh floor. It will be very quick.*

YOU: *Have you planned when you would do it?*

JIM: *I'd rather not say. Maybe I should wait until they lay me off. I mean I don't really care for myself, but I would love to upset them for the worry they've caused everybody* *with their doom and gloom. And I'm the expert on doom and gloom.*

You know that suicide is a definite risk. He has a plan, the means of carrying it out, and is not willing to discuss the timing of suicide. The fact he is withholding information that could be used to disable the plan adds to your concern. You know that he has had mental health care. You ask about the other risk factors.

YOU: *Have you ever tried to kill yourself?*

JIM: *No. I sure have thought about it though.*

YOU: *Does the pain of living with depression seem unbearable at times?*

JIM: *Yes, but it is more like the pain of being dead already.*

YOU: *Jim, who can you talk to about this, or about anything?*

JIM: *No one. Pearl and I don't talk. I don't see the kids. There's nobody. Look I shouldn't be telling you any of this. It's unfair to you. I've got to get a grip.*

It seems clear to you that if you combine this *risk* information with the alcohol overuse, the situation is very dangerous. It is time to find out if there are any life forces strong enough to support a *safeplan*. It is very likely that immediate supports will be needed.

YOU: *I'm glad you are talking to me. It sounds like you wish it would get better.*

JIM: *It can't.*

YOU: *Would you like to get better?*

JIM: *It won't get any better.*

YOU: *I know it seems that way, but would you like it to?*

JIM: *(silence)*

You may be his only resource at the moment. There is perhaps a hint of ambivalence in his silence, but you can't count on that. You decide that you don't want to let him go home alone.

YOU: *Jim, we have to get you some help and we need to do it now. I hate to see you suffering like this. I think you are in danger.*

JIM: *It's no use.*

YOU: *I know it seems that way to you, but we've got to try. Can we get hold of the psychiatrist you saw before and get a referral to someone here?*

JIM: I suppose I could call her. Too late now, but maybe tomorrow.

YOU: Will you promise me that you won't harm yourself between now and tomorrow when we talk and phone the psychiatrist?

JIM: Please, I can't promise anything. You have no idea how bad this is. I can't get a hold of anything hopeful. Look, please just go and leave me alone. I'll be fine.

You try to regain perspective by reviewing in your head and then you decide just to say your thoughts out loud.

YOU: Tomorrow is too far away. I think that's all you're really telling me. I think some part of you must want to live or you wouldn't be talking to me. If you really didn't want me to know, you could have found a way to do it more convincingly. It is like you are telling me to leave with one hand and holding on to me with the other. I need to find a more immediate safeplan, something that requires only minimal cooperation on your part. If I drop it now, suicide is even more likely. You probably wouldn't open up again. Something needs to be done and done now. I'm not going to leave you Jim, not like this. Look at your tears. You are really hurting. What I want us to do will seem difficult, but I think it might help.

JIM: (silence)

YOU: I want us to go to my car and drive over to the hospital together.

JIM: The hospital!

YOU: Yes. They can provide a safe place at least. They might know where we could get some help. And they could likely get in touch with the psychiatrist you saw easier than we can.

JIM: What good would that do?

YOU: I don't know, but we've got to try.

JIM: I just want to sit here and drink.

YOU: We both now know there is more going on than that. I'm going to go over with you and I'll stay as long as you want me to. Come on, let's go to my car.

JIM: But work?

YOU: I'll take care of work. They don't need to know what's happening unless you want them to. Come on, let's go to my car.

You stand up to indicate your willingness to **follow-up** on your *commitments* from the *safeplan*. Jim takes a deep breath, nods, and stands up also. He agrees to go with you.

Persons at risk can be friends, relatives or workmates. Emergency suicide first-aid can be useful anytime, anywhere. Jim is still strongly leaning toward death but he has heard and accepted your offer of help. Sometimes it is important to be firm and direct in order to save a life. The hospital is an appropriate place to ensure his safety and to access other supports.

Persistence, When You Most Need It

You are the parent of a 17 year-old boy, Guy, whose girlfriend killed herself two weeks ago after they broke up. He has been drinking heavily since the funeral. Your son was gone most of last night. This morning he seems sober, but you see him headed out into the farm-yard with his gun.

You're frightened. Her suicide has made you realize just how much he means to you. Your son knows that guns and booze are an extremely deadly combination... and he's mixing them deliberately. You can't afford to deny that he could be in grave danger. You calm yourself. You try to keep the accusatory tone out of your voice as you **explore** these possible *invitations* to help your son.

YOU: *What are you planning to do with that gun, Guy?*

GUY: *(silence)*

This isn't going to be easy. Things have been up and down, perhaps more down, as he has moved through his teenage years.

YOU: *You look upset enough to do something with that gun.*

GUY: *Don't worry. I wasn't planning to use it on you.*

YOU: *Guess you feel pretty awful about Renée.*

GUY: *I never should have broken up with her.*

You know that Renée's suicide was devastating for your son. The question is, what is he planning to do about it? You try to focus on feelings.

YOU: *You'd think you were to blame for the whole thing.*

GUY: *Why not? I get blamed for most things... and, she did write the note to me.*

YOU: *But, this time you're not responsible. Guy, she made her own decision.*

GUY: *Easy for you to say.*

YOU: *Is that why you've been drinking so much?*

GUY: *I'm drinking so I won't feel the pain. It doesn't work.*

The *invitations* could not be more obvious. You know what you are supposed to do now. You just never thought it would happen this close to home. You decide to **ask** directly about *suicide*.

YOU: *Are you planning to use the gun on yourself?*

GUY: *Yeah, I am.*

YOU: *When are you planning to do it?*

GUY: *Tonight.*

YOU: *Where?*

GUY: *Down at the lake. I don't want to make a mess. God, I don't believe I'm saying this to you.*

You attempt to separate his feelings from the drinking.

YOU: *Maybe the drinking is making it worse than it is. Maybe it's clouding your judgment.*

GUY: *How can it be worse?*

YOU: *It would be a lot worse if you were dead too.*

You attempt to uncover any signs of ambivalence in him.

YOU: *Is that what Renée would want — for you to kill yourself too?*

GUY: *No. She wanted us to live happily ever after.*

YOU: *Are you trying to get back at her?*

GUY: *No. I'm trying to get back to her.*

You offer support, although you are almost overcome by tears.

YOU: *I know we haven't gotten along very well these past months, but I do love you very much. I would feel terrible if you completed suicide.*

GUY: *I'm not trying to hurt you.*

YOU: *Graduation is close. You have a life ahead of you.*

GUY: *I could care less.*

You found out that suicidal thoughts and a plan are present — and that the plan is almost immediate, You know you must try hard not to be judgmental. You suspect that you are trying a little too hard at this point to find the *reasons for living*. Maybe you should try **listening** to the *reasons for dying*.

YOU: *So all the pain — and guilt, if I am listening carefully — is just too strong. If feels like you must kill yourself to make this right, or at least, it is the only way you can see to get the pain to go away.*

GUY: *Yes. You know, it really wasn't that I didn't care about her. There was probably enough there to have made it work but we were just so different on some things. She was all for family now. It did not matter to her what kind of job I might get, just so long as it paid okay. She wanted me to work for her father you know. I wanted.... Why didn't I just try harder. To hell with what I wanted.*

YOU: *You try to think through this and then the guilt and confusion about it all leads you back to suicide?*

GUY: *I guess so.*

"Guess" is different. Is that the part that wants to live trying to speak?

YOU: *Is there a part of you that would like to be less confused or that thinks that your guilt might be rushing you to judgment?*

GUY: *I don't know. I don't know. I don't know.*

You want to see if you have been **listening** to the *reasons for living* accurately.

YOU: *Basically, then, the answer is yes but it is very hard to hold on to any hope?*

GUY: *Yes, I guess so.*

There is some ambivalence. You already know what you need to know to **review** the *risk*. Your son has never tried to kill himself before nor has he ever received mental health care. Obviously, he is suffering pain that feels unbearable and he has shut off from any support right now. You work out what you want in the *safeplan*: remove the means, stick by him and not leave him alone for the next 24 hours and stop the alcohol use. It would also be good if you can get an agreement to call in professional help.

YOU: *Guy, this is really serious. I want you to give me the gun. If you don't, I'm afraid I won't see you again.*

GUY: *It's mine.*

YOU: *I know. But you are going through hell right now. And, not with the gun, and not now! Is that gun loaded?*

GUY: *No, the shells are in my pocket.*

YOU: *Will you give me the gun and the shells?*

GUY: *I suppose.*

YOU: *Now, please.*

GUY: *If you insist.*

YOU: *I do Guy.*

He hands you the rifle.

YOU: *And I want you to stay home tonight and not drink. I'm staying too. I want your promise on this. You're awfully upset; I think we may all need some professional help.*

GUY: *I don't want to do that.*

YOU: *Do what? Stay home or go for professional help?*

GUY: *Go for help. Look, I'm not crazy.*

Stay flexible. Take it one step at a time. Once he is completely sober and begins to talk, he will probably see the need for help.

YOU: *We will talk more about that part. I'm just glad you are prepared to stay home. That's a promise?*

GUY: *It's a promise.*

The first thing you want to do to **follow-up** on this agreement is to bring in a resource for yourself.

YOU: *Is it all right if I ask Uncle George to come over and stay with us? It's for me. I want his support.*

GUY: *Sure.*

This caregiver is full of courage and flexibility. The situation is a suicide in progress and she has an overwhelming emotional investment. Admire her persistence in working through the tasks, especially her ability to **listen** to the *reasons for dying*.

assisting

1	Connecting with a person who might be at risk is no different than what I do when I talk seriously to someone else about anything.	*True*. You could start with the weather or any other topic. Soon you come around to asking about the things that are happening in the person's life. If you know the person already, you know some of the things to ask about. If it begins to sound like she is distressed, you get more serious and explore what these "invitations" for serious talk might mean.
2	You have to wait for the right moment to ask about thoughts of suicide.	*False*. The right moment is whenever it occurs to you to ask. You can always explain why it occurred to you to ask right at that moment. If nothing else you could always say, "I just finished reading a book on suicide intervention and some of the things that you are talking about are sometimes connected with suicide. Are you having thoughts of suicide?"
3	Having someone to share the pain of dealing with suicide may be all that it takes to get past having thoughts of suicide.	*True and False.* If you have ever had a conversation about something that was bothering you with someone who could really listen, you know how much of a difference feeling understood by another person can make. Sharing the pain is one of the helping processes that can contribute to and lead toward agreement on an safeplan to avoid suicide. Although this and other processes are important, agreeing to a plan that keeps the person safe is the critical component in getting beyond suicide.
4	When it comes to safeplans, small steps, taken one at a time, are the key.	*A little bit False but mostly True*. As in everything else in suicide intervention, your judgment is important. One suggestion might be to include things for the person at risk to do that will also result in a sense of accomplishment once they are achieved. In most situations, this becomes: "small steps, taken one at a time." That is why "limited objectives" and "specificity" are usually good characteristics of a safeplan. If you are not sure a particular step is achievable, break it into smaller pieces, making sure that each of these can be managed successfully.
5	The chances that a person at risk will honor a safeplan commitment increases if the agreement is written down and both parties have a copy.	*False*. There is no evidence that written agreements are honored any more frequently than oral ones. For most of human history, all agreements were made orally. When paper was a rare commodity, more significance might have been placed upon written agreements. In contemporary times, paper agreements are sometimes seen as a sign of distrust among the parties to the agreement. Use written, oral or both formats when they strengthen the person at risk's sense of commitment and/or make the safeplan clearer. It is the person's stated intention to go along with the safeplan that is most important, not the form in which the statement is made.
6	I can't do an intervention.	*False*. After reading this handbook, you can't NOT try to do a suicide intervention when you recognize that suicide may be the issue. If you want to learn more, attend an *Applied Suicide Intervention Skills Training (ASIST)* or some other hands-on, practice-oriented learning experience about suicide intervention skills.

true and/or false

Preparing for Your Suicide Intervention Role

You may have been thinking about what it means to be a person who knows something about suicide intervention. What will it be like to use this knowledge over time with many different people at risk? Beyond the new challenges and learning associated with suicide intervention itself, there are other issues that will arise as you assume the role of a first-aid suicide intervener. Addressing these issues early in your suicide intervention career can bring comfort, extra confidence and better skills to every intervention.

Opportunities and Limits

With appropriate training and support, people from all walks of life can assist in preventing suicide. The value of having many helpers in a community cannot be overstated. On the other hand, each helper must acknowledge the limits of her competence and training. It is important to know when we can help and when more assistance is needed.

Depending on a caregiver's role and level of training, the help she provides may cover a wide range of activities. The following checklist of intervention-related tasks (chapter 5 will list other prevention tasks) may assist in clarifying what you are prepared to do now. The tasks (•) are grouped under three functions: suicide recognition, suicide intervention and ongoing care. At the end of each function, there is a "hand-off" task (°) where care may be transferred to persons performing the next function.

Suicide recognition
- recognize when someone might be at risk and is inviting help;
- reach out and engage her in a supportive relationship;
- identify the presence of suicidal thoughts
° facilitate links with those who know suicide intervention

Suicide intervention
- help name the reasons for dying and for living;
- review risk;
- address and contain those aspects of the current situation affecting health and safety;
- facilitate links with family, friends and professional help;
° offer ongoing support yourself, complementing that offered by others

Ongoing care
- provide counseling, treatment or therapy;
° consult with and be a resource to others who do suicide intervention caregiving

Note that the actual tasks cross the boundaries between functions. The first three tasks of suicide recognition are, for example, the first three tasks of suicide intervention. A practitioner may well hand-off to herself at the end of an intervention and start counseling, treatment or therapy.

Training and Preparation

The function and task list highlights areas where you might seek further training to expand your caregiving role. On the other hand, it may help you decide what things you don't want to explore further. This kind of role clarification sets limits and focuses your energy on what you do best. It frees you from feeling responsible for the whole situation.

If you have attended the *ASIST* workshop, you know that its skills-based focus is designed to help caregivers become more effective first-responders. It has proven useful for those reaching out to family or friends as well as for people in more formal practitioner roles in helping those who they serve. If you have participated in the workshop, you are in a good position to recommend its value to other individuals or organizations.

If you have not attended some kind of intervention skills training and you think you need more skills in knowing how to help, you are probably not alone. Find out who conducts an intervention skills training (e.g., *ASIST*) in your community and make it a priority to attend. If you are part of a staff team, you could suggest that your organization host a workshop, using a recognized suicide intervention training program. A community, group or organization could be encouraged to sponsor or host such a workshop.

Best Practices and Standards of Care

The standard for judging the care offered a person at risk results from three interacting processes: 1) evolving best practices, often called peer-developed guidelines; 2) professional codes of conduct; and, 3) legally determined standards of care. Knowing about best practices and legal standards of care will make you a more effective caregiver. A professional caregiver needs to know about the applicable provisions of her own professional code of conduct.

From a best practices point of view, a person at risk may reasonably expect the services outlined in the functions and tasks list. (Look through it again from this additional point of view.) Level of training affects the best practices that caregivers should expect of themselves. A person

who has no exposure to suicide prevention information would not expect to be able to recognize suicide risk. A person who knows how to recognize suicide danger is often not able to do a suicide intervention without additional training. An ongoing care professional would be expected to be capable of performing risk recognition and suicide intervention tasks.

Legal standards of care are both laws passed by legislatures and legal precedents from court decisions. These standards of care, while usually consistent with best practices, often lag far behind them. In other words, standards of care often require less than is already known to be helpful. For example, legal standards stop a caregiver from assault, deceit, fraudulent misrepresentation, defamation of character, breach of contract, and violation of human rights. This is of little guidance since any caregiver trying to follow best practices is not likely to violate these standards. Other legal standards focus primarily on what could be called, errors of commission — if you do something, don't do it negligently.

Standards of care expectations do not demand perfection. If you have some idea of what you are doing (have training), document what you do and consult with others, you are likely doing the best you can, both under a legal standard of care and in your actual practice. Training serves two purposes. First, it prepares you to follow best practices and meet the standards. Second, it adds evidence that standards of care were met, should you find yourself in a situation where you need evidence to that effect. It is much easier to claim that you met standards of care when you can show that you know what the expected standards are.

An interesting area of legal development is what could be called, errors of omission. Increasingly, organizations providing intervention services are being held legally accountable if they haven't assured that staff is trained to meet best practice expectations. Practitioners, both legally and in their codes of conduct, are expected to know and use suicide intervention best practices. It is reasonable to expect that all institutions in positions of trust will eventually be required to deliver best practices. As the stigma and taboo surrounding suicide is removed, it becomes increasingly clear that suicide is a serious social problem that cannot be avoided by omitting it from awareness.

Community Resources

A key part of being prepared for suicide intervention is knowing your community's resources. *ASIST*'s model of resources is provided on page 51 of this handbook.

Prepare a list of resources for your community. Whether or not you organize them consistent with the model is unimportant. Remember to distinguish between resources available around the clock and those that aren't. Remember that informal resources are often more dependably available and sometimes more effective than formal resources. In other words, the help of family, friends, workmates or neighbors, for example, is often critical. Community service groups and organizations are often important sources of longer-term support and might be used creatively in an emergency. The Quick Reference section at the end of this handbook provides another way to organize your list of resources. It has a template for recording basic contact information on a wide range of resourcest.

Learning About Resources

Once you have a map of your community's resources, find out:

- what or who is available
- what help they offer and when it is available
- what experience and training they have in working with persons at risk
- how they may be contacted
- whether their services are limited to particular groups or areas
- how they have worked with people at risk in the past
- whether fees for service are charged
- if they focus only on crises and/or work with people longer term

Phone calls or meetings with various providers can improve understanding of what they offer and build trust. You might view this as building your ready-to-help network.

After you access community resources, you may be asked or want to maintain some continuing role with regard to a particular person at risk for whom you provided help. For example, a counselor may continue to offer general support to her client while someone with more specialized training provides treatment or therapy. As a parent or friend, you may develop a working partnership with a counselor or caseworker. As a teacher who has identified and referred a person at risk, others to include in the care network may be the school counselor and parents. Various persons in a school or work setting may also want to share their observations about a pupil or workmate who has seemed distressed or depressed lately.

A key element in these working partnerships is regular communication about the overall care plan and each partner's role within that plan. The person at risk also needs to be "in the loop," rather than talked about behind their back. This does not mean that each shares everything they know with everyone else. It does mean that they communicate sufficiently to maintain consistent life-links and life-assisting networks.

Providing information to the persons and groups in the informal support rings helps ensure that their desire to help can be fully realized. Include information on places where they can access support for themselves. Whenever possible, include the person at risk in these information sessions. This helps develop a working relationship between the person at risk and natural supports. It also involves the person at risk in learning how to be her own natural support.

Consultation Resources

A further important way of building resource partnerships for someone at risk is to consult with others. Whenever possible, consult with persons who have relevant knowledge and experience in working with persons at risk. When not possible, consult with others who are good listeners and whose judgment you trust. The willingness to consult is a sign of wisdom rather than weakness. Specifically, it can help you to:

- monitor your initial and ongoing review of risk
- balance the attention you give to pain and possibilities
- review your plans for care and safety
- clarify your current and ongoing role
- recognize when further help may be required
- clarify what next steps may be needed
- increase the range of relevant resources
- discuss thoughts, feelings and dilemmas in helping a person at risk
- address beliefs and values affecting your work

- identify and integrate learning from your caregiving experience
- consider broader family, organizational or community implications

Prepare for your consultation needs in advance. Identify appropriate sources of support before you become involved in suicide intervention situations. For professional workers, this may involve approaching a supervisor or becoming part of a case-management group.

Balancing Safety and Privacy

Any decision to talk with a third person about someone we are helping raises the issue of confidentiality. Others confide in us because they trust us to keep information privileged. Sometimes, they will say that they trust only us. And sometimes, when people disclose information about suicidal thoughts, plans or actions, they are reluctant to involve others and may even ask us to keep the conversation secret. How does the caregiver deal with this dilemma?

The short answer is that, in situations like this, safety always comes before privacy or privilege. It is critical to avoid any secrecy agreements with people about their suicidal thoughts or plans. In professional codes of conduct, disclosure of confidential information in situations involving harm to self or others is usually required. In practice, balancing safety and privacy is more complicated and the following may be helpful when you have to negotiate the boundary between the two.

- **Confidentiality inspires trust.** As a general rule, respecting confidentiality is a vital element in any relationship of trust. Breaching confidentiality should be restricted to those exceptional situations where life or safety is at risk.

- **Inform people of limits to confidentiality.** Preferably, this should occur at the very beginning of helping and be presented as part of the caregiver's commitment to the person's safety and well being. It is also advisable to announce supervisory and other relationships where confidential information will be shared.

- **Seek permission to talk with others when you consider it necessary to talk with another person or persons about things told to you in confidence.** It is important, wherever possible, to seek the permission of the person at risk in advance and to help them understand why involving others is important or required. If possible, involve the person at risk in the selection and seeking out of additional resources. If reasonable efforts to gain the person at risk's consent are unsuccessful and you remain concerned about their life or safety, you have an obligation to disclose your concern and act on your understanding of the risk.

- **Focus all disclosures on safety needs.** The information you share with others should be limited to that needed to get help and attend to the person at risk's safety. It should only be given to those who can offer direct help (for example: ambulance driver, paramedic, physician, counselor or a natural support resource).

- **Involve parents of children or young people.** A parent or guardian should be included when a person at risk is under the legal age of adulthood unless exceptional circumstances apply. (For example, if parents are inaccessible or their involvement may diminish the person's safety, the caregiver could involve someone else whom the young person trusts.) Involvement of a parent needs to be talked through with the young person, paying particular attention to situations where the parent or guardian may be perceived as part of the problem.

Getting Help From Others

In most suicide first-aid situations, you are likely to need the help of others. They may be informal supports familiar to the person or organized caregiving providers. There are three aspects to obtain help successfully from other caregivers: 1) work with the person at risk to prepare her for using help; 2) know your community's resources and establish partnerships with them, as discussed in the previous supplement; and 3) establish the referral.

If the person at risk is receptive to the resource, the chances are increased that the resource will be receptive to them and that it will be used effectively. You can help increase the likelihood that the person at risk will view the resource positively if you:

- inform the person at risk of your need to break personal and/or professional confidentiality if required to help make them safe from suicide
- seek their permission to get help
- adopt the attitude that the "expertise" to help a person at risk exists in many places. It is not restricted to a special resource
- identify resources that are meaningful to the person at risk
- inform them about the resource and provide guidance on how to use it, including hints on how to judge whether the resource is appropriate
- offer to assist them in getting to the referral resource or even to attend the first meeting, if required

You are more likely to enlist the support of the resource if you:

- help the person at risk select a resource that is appropriate
- know the resource and have previously developed a ready-to-help partnership with them
- have worked successfully with the resource previously

Regardless of whether you know the resource or not, you are more likely to obtain their help if you:

- engage them in exploring the help they can offer
- identify who you are, including a reference to any workshop or other training you have had in suicide intervention
- provide your risk review and safeplan. Be confident and specific, outlining the information you have
- listen and be sensitive to any signs of resistance or other barriers to them providing help
- are patient and persistent about your risk review and judgment that additional help is necessary. Underline your persistence, if needed, by letting them know you are keeping a record of your risk review, safeplan and request for help
- educate them, if need be, on the benefits of reaching out to someone at risk. Point out the rewarding side of being helpful
- commit to maintaining a positive attitude and encouraging approach to the prospective helper
- offer your willingness to contribute to the building of a network of life-assisting support for the person at risk
- specifically ask for their agreement to help
- notify them of a specific time when you will get back to them on follow-up actions or to keep informed about their efforts to help
- thank them for their willingness to be part of the life-assisting network in your community

What to Expect at the Hospital

For anyone needing care, a hospital emergency department (ED) can be a frightening place. We offer this orientation to the process with a few hints about what to expect. We don't know whether you are arriving alone, have come with a caregiver or an informal support, or have been brought to the hospital by the police or ambulance. In the following, we will assume that you have come on your own because you feel at risk of harming yourself. If others whom you trust are there with you, they may help with parts of the process.

The first step is to make the ED aware you are there. Approach the main desk and someone will ask you to tell them why you need emergency care. Be certain to use the word suicide. Don't expect them to want to know very much. Their job is to assess the urgency of your problem and direct the next steps. If there has been physical injury, you will be escorted to a bed or cubicle and a nurse will begin the process of monitoring your physical state. Otherwise, you will be moved to a clerical station where a record of your visit is created. Identification and insurance information are needed. This document is for hospital caregivers to record the details of their observations, treatments and plans for your care. Unless you have a serious injury, you can't move forward without this paperwork.

Because the ED is often busy, the next stop is usually the waiting room. Complex decisions about who to respond to and when are taking place constantly in the ED. They haven't forgotten you, but they won't take time out to tell you that. Patience is a necessary virtue.

Once a bed or cubicle is available, expect to be known as the person in Bed 3 or

supplements

cubicle A-4. This is impersonal, but not intended to be personally demeaning. It actually helps to protect your identity. It provides the staff with an efficient short-hand for keeping track of all the people in the ED. A Nurse responsible for your location will begin the assessment process by talking to you about your problem. This information will be written down, but be prepared to repeat it a number of times to different hospital staff. Sooner or later, you will see an Emergency Physician, not a Psychiatrist as you might expect. The ED is the domain of this Doctor and her colleagues. Their job is to learn the story of what brought you to the ED, establish whether or not there are medical concerns (physical injury, overdose, intoxication), and decide whether or not you need to be referred for more intensive examination by psychiatry emergency staff.

Be as accurate as possible when asked to describe your problem. No one will likely have all the details, but it is extremely helpful if someone else who knows your current situation and past history is available to aid in telling your story. Often, to ensure that there are no medical concerns needing attention, a number of examinations or tests may be "ordered" by the Emergency Doctor. Accomplishing these may mean going to other sites in the hospital or meeting other hospital caregivers — and more waiting in the waiting rooms.

The staff is trying to decide what your problem is and what has caused it. This may all seem obvious to you, but it isn't to them. They need to arrive at a correct conclusion or proper diagnosis. Without this, they won't know what the right treatment is nor will they be able to communicate effectively with others who provide the treatment.

The treatment the staff suggest may be a referral to resources in the community. It can be very frustrating to wait and then be told that the most appropriate source of help is in another place or may not be available for days or weeks. Do not hesitate to ask questions or seek assurances that your problem meets criteria for being involved with these ongoing resources. Be sure that you have all the details about this new helping resource before you leave. Temper any frustration you have now with the knowledge that you have obtained access to what could be a very valuable community resource for you.

The treatment staff may recommend further specialized examinations by mental health caregivers. Psychiatry/Mental Health involvement does not mean you are "crazy." These professional caregivers are experienced in making a more detailed review of suicide risk and in developing complex safety plans. Often, you will be asked many of the same questions again as these new caregivers get to know you. A mental health assessment can take from 15-90 minutes. It is an in-depth examination of your mental state and your present and past history. Some questions may feel uncomfortable, but the caregiver should always be respectful and supportive of your emotional state. The primary reason for this assessment is to determine whether or not you are safe to leave the ED, whether a mental disorder is contributing to your current problem and finally to plan appropriate interventions to resolve the situation. Making these decisions requires having as much information as possible. Important others in your life may be contacted and your consent to obtain the opinions and records of other or earlier involved caregivers may be requested. Your cooperation and that of others will greatly aid this assessment, but it may take several hours to gather all that is needed.

During this time, you may be offered support in the form of medication or a move to a quiet space away from the medical treatment area of the ED. Depending on your cooperation, hospital security helpers may be involved to assure that you and others remain safe.

The outcome of the assessment and any treatment recommendations must always be presented to you. The suggestions for help should include all of the safety plan elements discussed in this chapter. Do not hesitate to offer your own ideas or to ask for more information about any suggestions. The plan must be reasonable and acceptable to you. It should offer some relief from current distressing situations and provide some immediate action to ensure your safety.

A plan for admission to a hospital or another care facility means that there is significant concern about your present safety. In a few circumstances, the Emergency Doctor or Psychiatrist has the legal responsibility to make you stay in such care, at least until a more complete assessment is possible. This can be unpleasant, but ensuring a safe space for you is the primary goal of such a plan.

If you are discharged, any ongoing care in the community should be confirmed, if possible, before you leave. If you believe that the assessment has failed to understand the life-threatening nature of the situation, restate your concerns until you feel they are adequately understood. The final outcome should be a workable plan that can be followed through with a good chance of success.

There is a final note of caution. Hospital ED's are staffed by caregivers who spend their working lives dedicated to preserving and saving life. They do not always succeed but most are prepared to do heroic actions to reach this goal. For a few of them, a person who is considering ending her life causes them conflicting feelings. They may find it difficult working on your behalf and appear to you to be non-supportive or even disrespectful. They may not appreciate that a person at risk is in the ED because she is seeking help to preserve and save her own life. If you encounter such a caregiver, focus on your needs for further care and safety. Seek the support you need from other caregivers responsible for your care.

Deciding When an Intervention is Needed

The six tasks outlined in this chapter are part of a unique model designed specifically to guide suicide first-aid interventions. Though it is obvious that parts of the tasks are similar to other helping processes, the whole model is only meant to be used in suicide intervention situations. This supplement explores some situations in which it may be less clear whether or not an intervention is needed.

In one sense, it would seem strange to attempt to use the model with people who are not having thoughts of suicide. While suicidal thoughts and behaviors are very common, many people experiencing very stressful situations will not consider suicide. There may be some who never think about suicide in their entire life. There will be some who do so only fleetingly. Sometimes you could actually damage a relationship by insisting that someone is having thoughts of suicide when she is not. Such insistence can ruin the opportunity to provide the kind of help the person actually wants. The possibility of such a negative outcome is even greater when suicidal intent is assumed to be unconscious. Persons who smoke, abuse drugs or drive recklessly, for example, will often deny that any suicidal intent is associated with these dangerous life-style behaviors. While some investigation of the possibility of suicidal thinking is quite appropriate, to insist in treating some activity of theirs as suicidal when the person refuses to accept that definition, is self-defeating and disrespectful.

In other situations where suicide is initially denied, the person may be open to the possibility that suicidal thinking may exist under the surface or occur in the future. Persons in distress, particularly persons with prior suicidal behavior, can often appreciate that there is a reason to be concerned about suicide. If the person acknowledges this possibility, it makes sense to develop a safeplan, should the need arise. You should acquire risk review information to help decide on the details of your safeplan. If the risk review information indicates that the person would have many risk alerts if she were to have thoughts of suicide, a more detailed safeplan would be appropriate. Usually, a simple promise to contact you should thoughts of suicide occur may be all that is required. Such "preventive" suicide interventions not only protect against suicide, they make the reapplication of the model easier in the future since suicide has already been treated as a subject that is appropriate to talk about.

You may be able to put preventive measures into place even though the person is totally opposed to regarding her situation as suicidal. Instead of calling your activities a suicide intervention, develop a safeplan to protect against an undefined "danger." Avoid a "power struggle" over what the danger is called and work toward an agreement that protects against the unnamed danger and suicide.

Another type of situation that raises doubts about whether or not an intervention is appropriate, is the person who threatens suicide or even harms herself but does not appear to consider suicide seriously or have any intent to die. The most

appropriate — and safest — response to either of these situations is to do a suicide intervention.

Persons engaging in these types of behavior are sometimes regarded as "manipulators" who only want some concession and are using suicide to get it. There is a more effective perspective for starting such an intervention. It recognizes that almost all persons who are suicidal have some hope for another alternative — an alternative that they want you to help provide even if they are not fully aware of it. It is also important to recognize that using suicide to gain some concession is a risky behavior. In time, it is likely that the threat or the behavior will be ignored. At this crisis point, the person may turn to suicide as an option, particularly since suicidal thinking and behavior are so well rehearsed. In the immediate context, do a suicide intervention and provide the person with what is required to prevent the risk of self-harm. Include in that plan referral to a mental health or counseling practitioner. Helping the person at risk out of this dangerous pattern of behavior is complex and will require time but it will not occur if you do not respond to the situation seriously to begin with.

5
community

community

Without a belief that we can assist others to live, we can easily become resigned to the way things are and lose any possibility for improvement. Such a belief can motivate and guide our efforts for change. Shared beliefs are even more powerful. In this chapter, we look at some of the ideals and practical things involved in creating and sustaining a life-assisting community.

Throughout the chapter, you will find in the "clouds," a vision of an ideal, suicide-safer and life-assisting community described as if it already exists. We hope this will make it easier to imagine what it might be like. To reinforce that this ideal is possible, we have included relevant sections of the guidelines for national suicide prevention developed by the United Nations and World Health Organization (UN/WHO). These guidelines have been used by a number of countries as a framework for national suicide prevention efforts. Most of the text is written as if the suggestions for developing life-assisting traditions were for a large community. Don't let that fool you. The principles are the same for much smaller communities, such as an extended family or a small business. Have a look at "Where to Start" in the chapter supplements to this chapter for a list of things you can do even if it seems that you are the only person in your community with a life-assisting vision.

This is an example of the "clouds" you will find throughout this chapter.

The text inside these clouds is a vision of an ideal life-assisting community described as if it already exists.

I've been on the phone all morning trying, without success, to find suitable help for Jack. He recently made an attempt on his life and is still at risk. It was the same as last week when I was trying to recruit friends and fellow-workers for the suicide intervention skills training. "We know it's important," they said, "but not now; maybe later." You are exhausted.

[You lay your head down on the desk and the next thing you know...]

The sign at the entrance to this community says, "Welcome to Co-opville: A life-assisting community working together to make all of us safer from suicide." In this community people answer your phone calls, offer help and provide other options. Skill training workshops are oversubscribed. Workshop partici-pants volunteer to organize future training. Organizations offer their facilities free of charge for meetings and work-shops. People from all walks of life meet on a regular basis to plan and coordinate ways to make their community safer from suicide.

[You wake up rejuvenated.]

Goals/Outcomes

- Preventing premature death due to suicide across the life span
- Reducing the incidence and prevalence of other suicidal be-haviors
- Reducing the morbidity associated with suicidal behaviors

- UN/WHO National Strategy Guidelines, 1996

Developing Shared Beliefs

Shared beliefs can occur at any level — international, national, provincial or state, community, neighborhood, workmates, even your extended family. At the international level, suicide was often regarded as a mental health problem assigned to the WHO. The impact of suicidal behaviors on the well being of a community is now more broadly recognized. The UN, through collaboration with WHO, has published guidelines for creating and implementing national suicide prevention strategies. International and national injury control and prevention groups are looking at intentional harm as one of the leading causes of fatal and nonfatal injury in all parts of the world. Shared beliefs have helped to create policy and action strategies in many locations including Australia, Canada, England, Finland, Norway, Scotland and the United States. In these communities, shared beliefs brought concerned citizens together with political leaders and professional helpers to do something positive about reducing the tragedy of suicidal behaviors. Without exception, these efforts were started and sustained by the dedication of a few concerned individuals. The level at which you choose to get involved doesn't matter. What matters most is for people from all walks of life to convert their shared beliefs into common goals and outcomes for their community.

Our life-assisting community shares certain beliefs. It is a community that practices working together and mutual support. Our community is essentially hopeful, but it is also realistic. It values practical solutions but also ensures that such solutions fit with the greater vision. Our suicide-safer community believes that a sense of aloneness is a prime contributor to suicide and that a sense of belonging is the greatest protection against suicide. Another idea we have is that acceptance, openness and helpfulness should replace denial, secrecy and avoidance.

Organizing Principle

Equipping individuals, families and communities with the knowledge, skills and values to foster and maintain the general health and social wellbeing of themselves and their communities is essential.

These universal activities directed towards all members of the society should complement the continuing availability of specific interventions for known problems or at-risk groups.

- UN/WHO National Strategy Guidelines, 1996

community

Creating Suicide-Safer Communities

While it would be encouraging to believe that our community has already created a range of life-assisting programs, that ideal has not been achieved in many places. Even most programs focusing on wellness give little attention to suicide. More often than not, suicidal behaviors are denied, kept secret or avoided. In most communities, ignorance and an apparent lack of interest in suicide prevention remains. If your community fits this description, you will need to start from the beginning.

As adults of all ages create and recreate their future, they will sense that they do not journey alone. Children are included in celebrations of life and in rituals marking someone's death. The life stories of the elderly broaden the view of all. A collective wisdom develops about life difficulties and ways to pass through them. When some person's life and mental outlook narrows to the point where suicide seems the only way out, our community will use this wisdom to help him find a way through the difficulties.

People with mental disorders are supported rather than stigmatized. The impact of these disorders on individuals and families is openly accepted. Their difficulties will be seen as crises of the human spirit, often affecting the will to live as well as the capacity to live creatively. Approaches to help and healing draw on the best social, spiritual and medical resources available.

In our community, death, grief and mourning are acknowledged as part of living. They are not seen as conditions that individuals are expected to "get over" but important as life experiences that honor loss and provide an opportunity to teach about life and living.

Families caring for their children are not afraid to share their times of trouble or turmoil. They know that there are times when everyone reaches limits or feels inadequate. During such times there are informal and formal community supports that will not judge or blame but come to their aid.

A Lack of Knowledge and a Lack of Interest

The first step is to recognize the state of the community's unawareness about the impact of suicide on its health. A lack of interest is typical of a community that does not recognize the importance of learning more about suicide prevention. Literally, the community is not doing anything because it does not know that anything needs to be done. Once the problem of suicide is recognized and accepted, it becomes clear that your community has a need for suicide prevention knowledge.

In our community, suicide is understood to be part of the human condition. Members know that suicide becomes possible during times of pain, anger or aloneness. They are comfortable talking about those times. They share their concern for others who may be struggling to find meaning or relief from pain and aloneness. Everyone knows how to read invitations to help when someone is at risk and how to work with a person at risk to keep them safe.

Should losses to suicide occur, the community is trained to respond, focused on the goal of identifying those affected and supporting them in their time of loss. Crisis response teams and community guidelines for preventing further suicidal behaviors provide services to ensure that survivors are aware of available informal and professional supports. The coordination of community services makes it possible to create "safety nets" which identify those affected by the loss of a significant other to suicide.

The Beginnings of Change

The following figure illustrates changes that need to occur in a community becoming aware of suicide as a problem and some of the steps involved in creating them. There are two places to begin a process of change. One targets the entire community with basic information about suicide using print materials, audiovisual productions and other mass media. The goal is a sensitized and aware community that wants to take action. The other targets natural and professional caregivers. It aims to enhance these caregivers' understanding of risk recognition and intervention approaches so that they will be prepared to respond to suicidal behavior as the community becomes more aware of it.

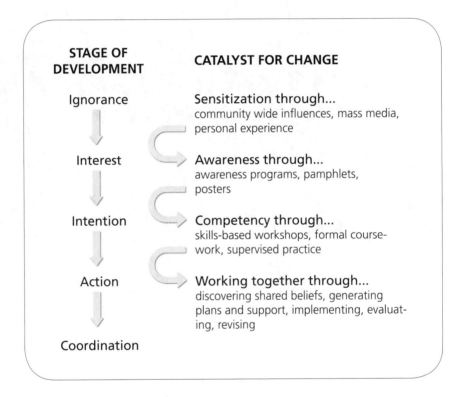

STAGE OF DEVELOPMENT

Ignorance

Interest

Intention

Action

Coordination

CATALYST FOR CHANGE

Sensitization through...
community wide influences, mass media, personal experience

Awareness through...
awareness programs, pamphlets, posters

Competency through...
skills-based workshops, formal coursework, supervised practice

Working together through...
discovering shared beliefs, generating plans and support, implementing, evaluating, revising

The basic information approach builds broad public support, increases understanding of at-risk populations and develops an awareness that prevention includes a wide range of actions. These developments may motivate a community to begin exploring ways to work together. In the initial enthusiasm surrounding these explorations, limited funding for various pilot or demonstration projects can often be found.

The next and most critical stage in the process of responding to suicide is to secure the commitment of enough secure funds to make longer range planning possible. In many communities, this stage is made difficult because the crisis management system within the community is split into many unorganized groups. Based on experiences around the world, the UN/WHO guidelines call for the appointment of a "lead agency" to serve as a coordinating organization. Using an already existing agency is better than creating a new one. The creation of a new super-organization specializing in suicide within the community would set up the same old message: suicide is so difficult that only experts can deal with it. It does not matter whether the lead agency is a part of the government or outside of the government. What is most important is that the lead agency wants to work with others in the community despite the differences that may exist. The following, adapted from a WHO guideline on general injury prevention, outlines what a lead agency needs to do and who they need to involve.

- obtain the approval of a cross-section of the community
- obtain the lead agency's commitment to involve a network of community caregivers
- include the health care community
- overview the part the community's organizations and personnel might provide
- address all ages, surroundings, and situations
- address the concerns of higher-risk groups
- adopt ways to document suicide and self-injury behaviors
- commit to a long-term approach
- design evaluation methods that include indicators of effectiveness and provide information on progress
- tell others, both nationally and internationally, about your community's experience with suicide prevention

Objectives for Creating a Suicide-Safer Community

The WHO/UN national strategy guidelines provide a list of things that need to be done. Not all need to or should be done by the lead agency. Responsibilities for achieving these objectives can be shared across many levels of concerned groups and individuals.

- adopt standard definitions of terms for suicidal behaviors
- increase public and professional access to information
- promote early identification, assessment, treatment and referral of persons at risk
- promote and/or support the establishment of an integrated data collection system
- promote public awareness of mental well-being and suicide safety
- develop or maintain a comprehensive training program for caregivers of all kinds
- adopt guidelines for the public reporting of suicide
- provide services to persons affected by suicidal behaviors: persons who are at risk or who have attempted suicide; their family, friends, colleagues and other associates
- reduce available, accessible and attractive means for suicidal behaviors
- promote and coordinate research, training and service delivery with respect to suicidal behaviors

community

Our life-assisting community knows that education and training is essential. It is quick to draw upon expertise, wherever it comes from. It does not want to pay the costs of "reinventing the wheel" or have something less than the best training possible. At the same time, it looks for expertise that enhances local resources. It does not want to become dependent upon outside expertise. It wants to work with outside expertise to build local expertise.

Caregivers are recognized as requiring special care and support themselves. They have learned to work together with others, draw on community resources and seek support, advice and feedback. They feel supported in their caregiving role. They are encouraged to balance their caregiving roles with time for themselves.

Should a caregiver experience a loss to suicide they know about the resources available to them since they have been involved in helping others connect to those resources.

Although well-developed and fully implemented suicide prevention strategies at the community level are not common, there are some good examples. If you want to know more about these initiatives, your best resource is the internationally recognized Suicide Information and Education Centre (SIEC) in Calgary, recently reorganized as the Centre for Suicide Prevention (CSP). The SIEC division houses a collection of information, and provides database searching and document delivery service to users anywhere in the world. SIEC, itself, is a good example of a program that can be quickly integrated as a core component of suicide prevention in your community. LivingWorks' *ASIST* training is another example of an existing resource that can be integrated or adapted to address the suicide prevention objectives of a particular community. Once a lead agency/group has been organized or approved in a community, the advantages of integrating such resources as SIEC and LivingWorks can be examined. Taking the time to search beyond the community for resources is a way to minimize the risk of re-creating elements that are already well established and in fully developed form.

The naming of a lead agency and adoption of the principle of working with others indicates that a community seriously intends to address suicide prevention and wants to avoid the pitfalls of a fragmented system. Planned work can now begin.

Take Action

Early identification of persons at risk and early intervention to prevent the immediate risk is one of the most important parts of a suicide-safer community. There are two approaches to early identification and intervention. One is to focus on selected higher risk groups and design identification strategies to find and refer them to appropriate resources. The other is to prepare caregivers and helpers throughout the community to identify and provide on-the-spot help to anyone at risk. LivingWorks adopted this latter, training approach as the most effective and efficient way of ensuring that *all* persons at risk of suicide could receive appropriate help.

Caregivers trained in suicide intervention are essential. Strategies that focus upon early identification of persons who might be at risk are likely to produce unintended negative outcomes without this training: persons at risk are identified but then placed in contact with resources who may be unprepared to help them. Adopting standards of care and best practices early in the development of the community-based approach is one way to encourage caregivers to obtain training. Informing the community about these standards helps to establish basic care guidelines. These expectations, in turn, create more incentive for caregivers to obtain training.

While early identification and intervention are critical parts, there are many other things involved in creating a suicide-safer, life-assisting community. The supplements to this chapter provide a sense of the range of helpful things to do. Let your imagination run wild: a funeral director is sensitized

community

to the stigma and taboo surrounding suicide; a parent encourages preventive education programs in the school; a police force develops a policy for receiving and storing firearms; a newspaper publisher develops a policy for reporting on suicides; a high school principal initiates a committee to review school policy; a community group sponsors an intervention skills workshop; a parent bereaved by suicide seeks government action to prevent suicide; a businessman seeks donations from other businesses to support the work of an interagency committee; etc.

Take Action Together

The best coordination strategy makes use of existing institutions and community resources of all kinds. It promotes agreements between these agencies and services to distribute and upgrade resources used to put the plan into practice. One agency may agree to do most of the intervention training, another to undertake bereavement services. A crisis response team may be made up of persons within an institution along with other members from particular agencies that specialize in providing these services. A review committee may consist of representatives from professional helping resources and volunteers from the community at large.

> *In our life-assisting community, collaboration is a central process. Each agency and caregiver does what they do best. Everything is coordinated through an interagency committee that has power to make decisions and to transfer funds to support those decisions. All caregivers know what to do, what others do and who to transfer to when their limits are reached. Everything is written down and the practices are examined frequently to make sure they are working.*

Working together includes a range of connections from cooperation through coordination to collaboration. The kind of working together that is most effective will evolve at a pace and in a direction determined by the participating members. Some ways in which connections might evolve over time include:

- meeting informally to exchange information
- formalized interagency cooperation but without the establishment of an interagency structure
- established interagency committee to coordinate activities but staff or representatives assigned to participate at the interagency level are expected to maintain primary loyalties to their home agencies

- participating agencies give the interagency unit the authority to set interagency policies and directions. Staff or representatives assigned to participate at this level of collaboration are authorized to give primary loyalty to the interagency mission, not to their home agencies

Informal or formalized cooperation arrangements are frequently the only concrete activity of interagency meetings. Another level involves formal coordination or collaboration agreements that allow an interagency committee to set policies, determine who will do what and establish the procedures for referral. A permanent interagency advisory committee may be needed to monitor and promote cooperation and coordination.

Organizing Principle

The mosaic of community resources for suicide prevention operates most effectively when their activities are coordinated and integrated. Collaboration at an intersectorial and interregional level, between government and nongovernmental organizations, and involving public and private sector contributions is also of fundamental importance.

- UN/WHO National Strategy Guidelines, 1996

There are still many attitudinal and practical barriers to the kinds of connections that are needed for a suicide-safer community. A new approach to advancing community-based plans is to sharpen and reinforce the working-together skills that are the foundation for more formal coordination efforts. This focus is on strengthening direct helper-to-helper connections and the fundamentals that make effective connecting possible. LivingWorks has worked closely with Placer and Los Angeles counties and the California Institute of Mental Health to develop this approach and with groups in Calgary and Ottawa to use it to improve the way helpers and other caregivers make day-to-day connections with each other.

Our community promotes help seeking and ensures that adequate help is provided. Every person's caregiving potential is encouraged. At the same time, the skills of professionally trained workers are acknowledged and utilized. People from all walks of life recognize that they have roles and responsibilities to play in promoting suicide safety.

community

Be Able to Show That Your Programs Work

Developing, testing and evaluating the effectiveness of the community's programs is strongly recommended as a key part of any suicide prevention effort. As various parts of the plan are created and put into practice, built-in feedback procedures should check that the results are consistent with the aims. Plan for regular reviews of progress. Spot-check the effectiveness of various programs early in their implementation. For example, you may wish to determine whether or not certain messages are reaching most of the community and how they are being received. Or, as another example, you may wish to know if certain referral arrangements are working.

In our community, we recognize successes and acknowledge achievements. Evaluation of how things are done, as well as whether goals are met, is ongoing. While we are always looking for ways to improve, we are careful to encourage things that work. We constantly draw upon the world literature, but we also put new ideas to the test. Part of that test is how a new approach will affect everything else we do.

Plan for a more thorough evaluation. While the ultimate aim of a comprehensive suicide prevention plan is a reduction in the number and severity of suicidal behavior, do not base your evaluation efforts on that goal alone. Some aspects of suicidal behavior are subject to factors over which you can have no control. You may have the best program in the world and still have the rate of suicidal behavior remain constant because of the economic situation, the characteristics of new immigrants entering the community, or a host of other poorly understood factors. Instead, focus attention on gathering data about actions and activities such as the number of interventions being made, the community's beliefs and values about suicide, the number of referrals being made, the number of bereaved receiving help, and the number and nature of crisis situations receiving a response. Also gather data on the outcome of these activities. For example, what was the outcome of the intervention? How do the parties feel about it? If a referral was made, was it appropriate? What was the long-term outcome of the intervention?

Sooner or later, funding will be challenged. Ongoing evaluation helps you to develop the best program possible and provides evidence to support continued funding.

Conclusion

Most of this handbook has focused upon suicide intervention. As a caregiver, you may be the last line of protection when life or safety is at risk. This work as a suicide first-aid caregiver can continue on your own will power whether or not it is supported in your community. Your work will be more sustainable and more rewarding, however, the more that your community becomes like the one our dreamer envisioned. Help to create a community that you want to belong to and get a double benefit: a sense of belonging is also life-assisting.

Our community is proof of the power of the individual to create change. Sustaining that power is the belief that there are common values among many people in the community that just need to be uncovered and activated. Our ideal community has many individuals able to sense the common concern and inspire it into common action.

community

1	The person dreaming is being idealistic and unrealistic.	*True and False*. As you follow the dreamer's story, it is true that some of the things that the dreamer wants do not exist yet — at least in technology-based cultures. But, who knows the future and the potential of human kind? On a more realistic note, many of the things that the dreamer dreams can be and have been done. Without taking away from the dedication of the persons who made those dreams come true, if much of it can be done several times — and it has been — why not more times?
2	The place to start is with a few basic facts about suicide.	*True*. Start with a simple agreement that suicidal behaviors are a problem — and a not so simple understanding of what that means. The majority of the population believes that suicide should be prevented; but there is an unwarranted pessimism that suicide can be prevented. It is tragically clear that suicidal behaviors are a significant problem that can be reduced and for which society provides very few resources.
3	Creating a suicide-safer community is easy.	*False.* After spending a lot of time working in this area we know how much is involved in making a good start. Often it is amazing — and terribly sad — how little is known and done. The sadness often stems from the fact that it takes an unusual increase in suicides in a region or organization before that community becomes sensitized to a problem that already exists. It is even sadder when this recognition finally generates activities that are less than what is known or are doomed to have little effect.
4	Cooperating is complex.	*True and False*. Indeed, there is a lot more to cooperating than you might at first think. Part of the contemporary apathy about so many things stems from the realization that many things really are quite complex. On the other hand, cooperation is really quite simple. Human beings have been cooperating since the dawn of time. We know at a "gut level," how to do it, when it is happening and when it isn't. The hardest part is to maintain a commitment to being cooperative when there are so many opportunities to gain individual advantage.
5	It is difficult to maintain enthusiasm for all of these aims and at the same time adopt a strong, scientific approach to achieving them.	*True and False*. It is hard to be both the one who encourages positive emotions and the hardheaded scientist at the same time. One solution is to involve others who are more inclined toward that which you are less inclined. Another is to remember that both are important and stem from the same basic motivation: the determination to make a difference.

true and/or false

Where to Start?

If your community is not sensitized to or aware of the problem of suicide, you may feel you are on your own with your desire to make a difference. We suggest a number of activities that might help you link with others just as concerned as you are.

- begin a discussion with someone about the size of the problem of suicidal behavior and/or the availability of community resources
- visit a funeral home and ask to see their resources on death and bereavement
- ask schools if they have guidelines in place for responding to suicides
- ask your local law enforcement agency about guidelines for restricting access to firearms
- contact your local emergency services to ask about procedures and follow-up for persons who self-injure
- contact your local crisis line and ask what resources for education and training they have available
- contact some of the resources at the end of this handbook to find out about training resources in your community
- organize a suicide awareness presentation or intervention skills training

Chapter 5 was written with the *ASIST* participant in mind. In addition to developing suicide intervention skills, *ASIST* is a very successful meeting place to uncover common concerns and to build relationships for addressing them. Building upon these partner-ships, you may wish to do some of the things from the list above. You might also find some useful ideas in the following list. It mirrors the content of chapter 5 in point form.

- prepare a community policy statement. Something as simple as, "Suicide is a serious public health problem in our community," will help you find others who might want to help
- make an inventory of services currently available including comments on strengths and gaps in services
- locate an interested "lead" agency or group willing to "take on" suicide prevention community development work
- organize a conference, workshop or focus group activity that invites community members to help document the "suicide situation" in your community
- circulate fact sheets containing current suicide statistics and include information on the frequency of suicide-related crisis calls to local crisis services
- distribute overviews of the WHO/UN guideline objectives for suicide prevention and the WHO Safe Communities Model
- focus on ways to motivate broad-based community interest and commitments to work together
- find ways of inviting and empowering instead of fueling competition over resources
- brainstorm creative ways of getting everyone in the community involved — donations of services, space, air time, including corporate and business support
- develop a comprehensive suicide prevention plan, mutually created and agreed to by key community players
- find funds to support persons who can organize meetings, keep on top of recent information, keep informed of community concerns and update the community on developments

- educate and empower significant community players so that eventually they become their agencies' resident experts
- set mutually determined goals and expectations that are reasonable and measurable
- work with a process that elicits ownership of the problem and solution, moving to written protocols and procedures only after the sense of ownership has been established
- use suicide intervention skills training to give everyone a common language and intervention and risk review tools. This will improve community communication and networking as well as create a solid resource base. Do this before introducing community awareness and prevention activities that increase the demand for service

More Shared Beliefs

Preamble from The United States National Strategy for Suicide Prevention — Recommendations (Reno, NV, 1998).

1. *Suicide prevention must recognize and affirm the value, dignity and importance of each person.*
2. *Suicide is not solely the result of illness or inner conditions. The feelings of hopelessness that contribute to suicide can stem from societal conditions and attitudes. Therefore, everyone concerned with suicide prevention shares a responsibility to help change attitudes and eliminate the conditions of oppression, racism, homophobia, discrimination and prejudice.*
3. *The groups we have categorized as diverse populations are disproportionately affected by these societal conditions and some are at greater risk for suicide. These groups include: Asian/Pacific Islanders, American Indians/Alaskan Natives, African-Americans, Latinos, Gay, Lesbian, Bisexual and Transgender populations.*
4. *Individuals, communities, organizations and leaders at all levels should collaborate in the promotion of suicide prevention.*
5. *The success of this strategy ultimately rests with the individuals and communities across the United States.*

Awareness Information or Intervention Skills?

Question: *What do persons in my community need?*

Awareness Information

An awareness program, like LivingWorks' *SuicideTALK*, can serve a number of purposes. These presentations are for persons interested in learning more about suicide and what can be done to help those at risk. They are designed to stimulate or build on concern about suicide. They often provide basic information about signs of suicide risk along with initial helping steps. Some address the needs of those bereaved by suicide. Sometimes, broader issues about how to create greater awareness in communities, schools and workplaces are discussed.

These programs usually provide basic information but do not offer opportunities to develop suicide intervention skills. Some find that attending an awareness presentation is sufficient for their needs and interest. Others choose to become more involved and recognize that they will need more skills to do this effectively.

Awareness presentations are shorter and aimed at a large number of persons. The goal is for members of the audience to identify ways that they can help. It is hoped that members of the audience will support suicide-safety and life-assisting programs in their communities and be more willing to refer persons at risk to helpers who are prepared to intervene. Most awareness audiences will recognize that there is more to learn before they feel ready, willing and able to intervene to prevent the immediate risk of suicide.

Intervention Skills

Suicide intervention training programs, like LivingWorks' *Applied Suicide Intervention Skills Training (ASIST)*, equip people to respond knowledgeably and competently to persons at risk of suicide. Participants learn and practice skills in identifying and responding to people at immediate risk of suicide. Just as "CPR" skills make physical first-aid possible, training in suicide intervention develops the skills used in suicide first-aid. Skills training programs should address caregiver attitudes towards suicide since these personal elements affect an individual's willingness to help and the effectiveness of the help offered. Such programs also typically explore options for linking people with resources for ongoing help.

Skills training programs are longer and aimed at persons in positions of trust. The persons best able to provide suicide first aid are the persons others turn to in times of trouble. In intervention skills programs, such persons are typically called caregivers or gatekeepers.

Intervention training programs are skills-based and provide a solid foundation for intervention and follow-up. Those participating in a suicide intervention skills workshop should leave feeling ready, willing and able to intervene to prevent the immediate risk of suicide. With this confidence, participants are often more willing to take a leadership role in suicide-safety and life-assisting programs.

Answer: *Both awareness and intervention skills are essential. Every community needs people who support suicide prevention as well as caregivers who are prepared to intervene.*

Preventing Suicide

The kind of preventive actions discussed throughout most of this handbook are specific intervention activities for persons with thoughts of suicide. These persons are in the river of suicide and may be close to the waterfall of self-harm. Other kinds of actions are taken before the onset of suicidal thoughts and the danger of a suicidal action occurring. Such actions are taken before the person is ever actually in the river; before ideas of suicide ever surface. These prevention strategies hope to reduce and even end any need for suicide first-aid or other treatment interventions.

There are two general approaches to preventing the development of ideas of suicide and subsequent suicidal behavior. One is to promote the development and maintenance of coping strategies that are adaptive and serve to maintain well-being. These may involve internal resources such as resiliency and self-esteem that enable a person to handle stress. The other is a protective strategy to minimize the development of conditions or circumstances that may lead to the appearance of suicidal ideation at a later time. For example, the early detection and treatment of depression should protect some people against the risk of suicide.

Some activities would be universal and aimed at everyone. Some would be aimed at selected groups. In the table below, targets or sites of activity for promotion or protection approaches are illustrated.

Targets and Activities for Promotion or Protection

	PROMOTION ACTIVITIES	PROTECTION ACTIVITIES
UNIVERSAL TARGETS	**Marital status** · relationship skills **Societal Messages** · life affirming, not violence · honesty and openness (no secrecy) · understanding and respect for all **Alcohol and Drug Use** · responsible use **Modeling** · nurturing living skills	**Methods** · restrict methods **First-Aid Intervenors** · caregivers trained in suicide first-aid **Media** · appropriate portrayals of suicide
SELECTED TARGETS	**Chronically Medically Ill** · support and endurance **Personality Disorders** · resiliency **Minorities** · stress management · community acceptance · cultural sensitivity	**Depressions** · recognition and treatment **Psychosis** · treatment and resources

There are a lot of activities that might accomplish these promotion and protection goals. Few have solid evidence to justify implementing them. Most make practical sense to experienced caregivers and to persons involved in the study of suicidal behaviors. Of the more promising, a number are being tried in pilot or demonstration projects to gather evidence that might justify their wider use. The most important conclusions about prevention are that it is possible (there are reasons to be optimistic), that a variety of approaches are needed because persons at risk are not all the same (a broad range of tools are needed), and that activities can begin almost anywhere and at any level of the community (complexity is not an excuse for failing to start). This brief overview of prevention activities is not intended to be complete. There are many more target groups and many more activities that might be applied either to a specific target group or universally.

School Policy

New Jersey Adolescent Suicide Prevention Project (1997) template policy:

Suicidal behaviors have been increasing in severity and frequency among children and adolescents. The Board directs that all school personnel be made aware of the identifying signs of these behaviors.

Suicidal behavior may not be apparent until a critical phase has been reached. School personnel must be prepared to spot at-risk students and to refer them to designated staff. Any such signs or the report of such signs from another student should be taken seriously and communicated immediately to the principal or other designated staff. Every effort shall be made to provide positive intervention by using available school personnel and the assistance of appropriate agencies on behalf of the student.

The student's parents/guardians shall be notified immediately of any suspected suicidal behaviors and their cooperation shall be sought in arranging for appropriate intervention.

If parents/guardians indicate an unwillingness to cooperate in the best interests of the student, the school administration shall contact appropriate administrative or legal agencies to request intervention on the student's behalf.

In-service and continuing education programs shall be made available to the professional staff to assist them in identifying the signs of suicidal behaviors. Staff members shall also take appropriate procedures for immediate assistance and intervention for the student.

The health education curriculum will address the topics of stress, depression and suicidal behaviors.

Written procedures shall be developed to deal with 1) observation of behaviors that indicate a student may be at risk of a suicidal act, 2) a student who has voiced or written an intent to engage in a suicidal act, and 3) a student who has attempted a suicidal act.

Addressing Concerns About a Suicidal Youth

Important people in a person at risk's life need to understand what having suicidal thoughts or behavior means about a person and his current situation. As an example, some of the following information might be relevant to helping parents understand the suicidal thoughts or behavior of their teen.

It is not uncommon for a young person to go through a crisis and experience suicidal thoughts. Sometimes young people have confused, romantic notions about death and do not fully understand the finality of it, but this is far less common than most realize. Suicidal intentions and behavior mean that something is wrong. The teen is experiencing pain although it maybe expressed in many forms including anger and revenge. Something is causing them so much distress that they will try anything, including suicide, to stop it. Suicidal persons often speak of death as a relief from a life too painful to bear.

The teen may feel ashamed and hopeless. Their ability to see problems objectively has gradually decreased. Their shame may keep them from others, leading to feelings of isolation. Some teens with limited life experiences may have difficulty believing that things will likely turn out all right. They may believe there is no other solution to their difficulties and that no one really cares about them.

Most teenagers who attempt suicide do not really want to die, but they do want to stop hurting. They need someone to realize they are in pain and to help them find solutions. They need someone with whom they can talk. They may need to learn better coping skills, including how to reach out to others and how to solve problems.

It is not uncommon for parents to be the last to know about their child's thoughts of suicide. Parents should not dwell on blaming themselves nor should they blame their child. Blame is only useful if it leads to problem solving. More often than not, blame leads to denial: it is all my fault or it is all their fault. Dealing with the problem openly, honestly, and compassionately is

most important. Understanding is the key to problem solving.

After a Suicide — Reporting on Suicide

Canadian Association for Suicide Prevention template for informing the media:

As suicide prevention professionals, we suggest that media coverage of suicidal behavior project an objective yet preventive message, as well as educate and inform the public about the subject. Many local media organizations agree that suicide should only be reported if: it occurred in a public place; the victim was prominent; or, it was a symbolic protest of some perceived wrong.

It is best to avoid reporting the specific details about the method of death, or give simplistic cause-effect reasons for suicide, such as "Teen kills himself to avoid jail sentence," or "Boy kills himself because of braces" or cultural stereotypes (e.g. "Chinese man kills self"). Although we feel that downplaying the suicide story would be desirable, we realize that this is not always possible because of the news value of some suicide stories.

Instead, suicide prevention experts recommend that the media balance the possible negative affect a suicide story may have by publishing or broadcasting helpful information the reader/viewer/listener may use if they feel at risk or they know of someone at risk.

We also recommend that the media use terminology that projects a positive and preventive message about suicide whenever possible. As the following examples illustrate, choice of wording can have a positive or negative effect on your audience.

Avoid phrases like: "a successful suicide attempt," "an unsuccessful attempt," "suicide victim," "suicide-prone person" and "stop the spread/epidemic of suicide." Use phrases like: "a suicide," "a suicide attempt," "a person who died by suicide" or "a death by suicide," "person at risk (of suicide)" and "help prevent suicide." "Suicide survivor" is the term commonly used by bereaved families/associations to denote a friend or family member of a person who died by suicide. It does not refer to a suicide attempter who did not die as a result of his/her attempt.

After a Suicide — Guidelines for the Community

Every community should develop and review a specific plan of action in advance of a death by suicide. Following are some elements that should be included as part of any after-suicide plan that treats suicide as a serious community health problem.

Setting Norms: Prepare community and/or institutional leaders to shape norms about suicide. These norms should emphasize openness and understanding, without condemning or glorifying the suicidal event or the person. Such norms will help to bring suicide out into the open where it can be talked about and prevented. Factual information about the suicide should be shared promptly. This is the best way to reduce the spread of rumors that are often prevalent when a suicide occurs.

Institutions and organizations should be discouraged from holding large assemblies to announce suicidal deaths, provide information about the suicide, or memorialize the person who died by suicide. It is better to address the situation on a smaller scale in class or work group discussions where reactions can be discussed fully. Attendance at any memorial/funeral activities should be optional. Institutions and organizations should not be closed for the funeral. It is important for many that the usual routine continues in the days following the suicide. For others, the suicide represents the loss of someone with whom they were close. The staff, students or coworkers so affected may wish to attend the funeral and should be free to do so. Provide the affected persons opportunities for grieving and talking with others.

Reach out to Others: Identify close friends of the person who killed himself and offer special assistance to them. Help them realize that they were not the cause of the suicide. Deal directly with this common concern or fear. Set up discussion groups to provide opportunities for other people to ask questions and get truthful answers. Let people know that the person who killed himself was unhappy and that suicide is not the only option to unhappiness. Provide the opportunity and freedom for everyone involved to discuss feelings of sadness, guilt, fear, and/or anger.

Identify and engage others in the person's environment that are known to be at risk of suicide. Even if they did not know the person directly, news of the suicide can put them at greater risk following the suicide.

Assign a Central Spokesperson: All outside requests for information (including those by the press) should be referred to a single spokesperson. This person must have accurate and official information both about the suicide and about what the community is doing for those who are affected.

Work Closely with the Media: "Copycat" suicides, also known as "imitative suicides" or "clusters," are affected by the

"Werther effect" of media coverage. The term takes its name from Goethe's 1774 novel, The Sorrows of Young Werther, in which the hero kills himself. The book was widely circulated and imitative suicides were reported throughout Europe. Some people killed themselves while dressed as Werther. Others killed themselves in the same manner as Werther, with a copy of the novel open to the page describing his suicide. The effect of this publication and other similar reports after widely publicized suicides has led many researchers to believe that media attention given to a suicide may model the acceptance of suicide to others.

Depressed teenagers — impressed by the fame achieved through news stories, school assemblies, or memorial services — are known to have committed self-destructive acts to obtain similar attention for themselves. In 1986, the first large-scale study of imitative suicide showed that self-inflicted deaths and injuries increased after news stories about suicide — particularly among teenagers and particularly in the immediate geographical area. The study showed that the more publicity there was, the more imitative suicides occurred.

It should be noted that there is no evidence that suicidal thoughts are created in someone who was not previously suicidal or depressed. The effect occurs in those who have already been thinking of suicide. The danger of acting upon these thoughts is increased when others in the community carry out the act.

In working with the media, ways of reducing the potential harm of suicide stories must be promoted. The act itself needs to be de-glamorized and the availability of information about helping resources should be emphasized. Community news editors should be approached in advance. Explain the concern about the Werther effect and request that they carefully consider the impact of their coverage of suicide stories. Some of the following suggestions for minimizing the Werther effect may be useful in discussions with the media.

Ask them to avoid reports which sensationalize or romanticize the suicide. Try not to concentrate on the dramatic elements of the death or of an attempted rescue. Do not report specific details about the method of death or give simplistic cause-effect reasons for the suicide.

Encourage them to downplay the story by avoiding front-page placement or large headlines. If the story must appear on the front page, ask that it be placed below the fold. Avoid using the word "suicide" in the headline or printing a photo of the person who killed themself. Avoid repeated follow-up stories.

Ask them to mention the negative consequences of the suicidal behavior in terms of the pain suffered by survivors and the loss of the person's potential. Emphasize that there are alternatives to solving seemingly hopeless problems. Ask them to point out that positive outcomes can occur when people get help to avoid suicide.

Ask them to highlight information about resources available locally for people who feel suicidal. Include a list such as "when to be concerned" with advice about what to do when a person at risk is identified.

After a Suicide — Guidelines for School Settings

Every school should develop and review a specific plan of action in advance of a death by suicide. Written guidelines should be developed within the context of a school board approved, comprehensive, school-based suicide prevention policy.

Designate a Response Team: The response team usually involves the principal and counselors within the school. Consider who else might be involved (psychologist, school nurse, spiritual advisors, police resource officers). Parents and other volunteers can be of great assistance if they are oriented to the response plan in advance. Establish a chain of command. The principal is usually named as the primary person in charge. Students will respond best to people they know, as will staff. Also use an objective outside consultant. A member of the response team from another school can be an important resource for the response team who are on the front line dealing with staff, students, and parents.

Provide Accurate Information: Promptly share factual information about the suicide with staff members and students. This is the best way to reduce the spread of rumors that often arise when a suicide occurs.

Hold a meeting to brief staff members about the tragedy and to give them a chance to deal with their feelings about the suicide prior to working with the students. It is best for students to hear the news from a familiar person (principal, counselor, classroom teacher). Review the school's procedures for dealing with the tragedy and prepare staff members to work effectively with the students. This meeting is best conducted in the morning prior to the start of classes.

Staff may be called to a staff meeting during the day if that is when knowledge of the death occurs. It is usually best if staff are all together so that they all hear the same thing, but they could meet in shifts if there is a concern about leaving all classes unattended. It is best to make an announcement to students before they go home. Staff should attend a staff meeting at the end of the day to debrief reactions, problems, and concerns.

It is usually best if classroom teachers inform students using a prepared statement. Public address announcements should not be used. Large assemblies are inappropriate as they are too hard to control and don't provide students with the opportunity to respond. The use of a prepared statement is best as it gives teachers a way to make sure that everyone hears the same thing. If the suicide is not fully confirmed, acknowledge uncertainty by using the word, "apparently."

All outside requests for information should be referred to a single spokesperson who has accurate and official information about the suicide and what the school is doing to assist staff and students. All staff members should be instructed to direct outside requests for information (including those from the press) to this spokesperson. The principal and the spokesperson should discuss what details about the death should be made public. Consultation with the parents of the student who killed themself is a good practice.

Deal with Reactions: Because a suicide can result in self-destructive feelings in other students, special efforts should be made to prevent contagion. Encourage teachers to discuss the suicide in their classrooms after making the announcement. Following are some guidelines for teachers to use during those discussions.

Don't be impassive about a student's death. Share reactions with the class. Be careful not to romanticize the self-inflicted death. Inform students about funeral arrangements and offer tactful advice about funeral etiquette. Talk with students about their feelings. Let them know that it is normal to feel fear, anger, and confusion, as well as grief. Let the students talk and write about their feelings. Do not disagree with or challenge feelings expressed by students at this point. Listen to whatever students have to say. Never shut off discussion. If students ask questions of a religious nature, lead them to answers based on their own beliefs. Do not force a regular day on grieving students, but at the same time, do not allow the class to be totally unstructured. Explain how students might respond to a bereaved student who is returning to school. Point out the need to resume normal relationships. Remember that the class may be quiet and depressed or unusually noisy for some time afterward. Some students may begin to act out as a way of affirming that they are still alive. Leave some routine in place for non-grieving students and others who may appreciate a change of focus.

Establish a central area within the school to which students and staff can come to discuss their feelings, express their grief and lend support to each other. Have some response team members available in this central location. Make contact with students who were close friends of the person who completed suicide. Additional counseling should be offered to these students. Their parents should be made aware of the school's concern for them. Indeed, it is sometimes appropriate to take such friends out of class and have the response team inform and assist them individually or in small groups. Notify other schools where the victim has friends or siblings. The response team should identify other students who are known to be at risk of suicide and should make contact with them.

Contact the family of the deceased student. Immediate and caring home contact by the school administration and counseling team is particularly important in the case of a suicide because neighbors and friends may not know what to say or how to react. Family members may be experiencing a sense of isolation and a lack of support or understanding. Contact from the school might include expressions of sympathy and support, as well as suggestions for the funeral service. When appropriate, school personnel should gather together all the person's belongings at the school and give them to the family of the student who completed suicide.

Assist students to plan a living memorial that prevents future suicides. Help them to identify the pain that led to the death and to discuss other ways that students can cope with their problems. Take care that the memorial project does not romanticize or stigmatize the act of suicide. Later, prepare plans for possible reactions on the anniversary of the suicide and other follow-up needs. Review the response plan. Consider the need for additional prevention efforts or training.

After a Suicide — Significant Others

A suicide death will likely be the source of intense grief for everyone affected. The impact can be devastating, particularly for those who felt they had close emotional ties or special responsibilities to the person who died. A suicide can also send shockwaves through a school, workplace or community, affecting people who were never personally acquainted with the person who died.

Suicide can place a special burden on survivors. In addition to grieving, they must contend with the fact that this death was by suicide. In many communities, it remains difficult for caregivers and the bereaved to talk openly about suicide or to be supported by rites and rituals that facilitate mourning.

Everyone grieves differently. Survivor grief is affected not only by the circumstances of the loss and personality differences in the bereaved but also on the nature of the relationship with the person who died. It is important to respond in ways that respect these differences and recognize that grief has no prescribed timetable.

Despite these differences, there are common themes. Typically, first reactions of shock, disbelief and bewilderment are overtaken by painful and intense feelings as the reality of the loss sinks in. Gradually, people experience healing and find ways of living with the loss and reinvesting in the future. However, this journey toward recovery is not a straight-line pathway. Detours are common and people often find themselves revisiting painful memories and adjustments that they thought they had put behind them. This pattern has prompted some to refer to grief as a series of overlapping cycles centering on the themes of avoidance, confrontation and integration.

Avoidance: First reactions to a death by suicide are typically shock, disbelief and numbness. The individual may be dazed, confused and uncomprehending — going through the motions of each day but unable to focus or respond clearly to people, tasks or events. As the shock wears off, denial may linger to buffer the survivor from absorbing the full impact of what has happened.

Confrontation: Progressively, the reality and pain of the suicide and the loss sink in, evoking intense, often fluctuating, emotions. People may experience and express intense pain, anger, guilt and self-recrimination: "What more could I have done?" "Why didn't I catch the clues?" "Why wasn't I there when needed?" Sometimes the sense of relief that the person's suffering has ended is tinged with additional guilt. This guilt may be further compounded by the stigma and shame associated with suicide. A search for answers and meaning in the loss are practically universal.

Integration: Gradually, the bereaved come to terms with the reality and finality of the death and learn to live with the loss and the lingering sadness. People find ways of moving on, taking with them the legacy of the suicide and the bereavement experience but also engaging or re-engaging with people and activities that are meaningful for them. Sometimes the process of creating life without the person who died can arouse feelings of guilt. Often, the pain of the loss is periodically and sometimes surprisingly re-awakened, especially around special times — holidays, anniversaries, favorite songs, or familiar events. However, these experiences are usually less intense and less prolonged as time passes.

A comprehensive care plan includes procedures for identifying, contacting and helping those bereaved by suicide and addressing community attitudes and practices which affect healing after a suicide. On a personal level, the following elements are among those that promote effective bereavement support.

- reach out, connect and listen
- encourage the survivor to tell their own story
- review the circumstances surrounding the death
- recognize and respect diverse bereavement experiences and needs
- attend to feelings and the overwhelming need to know "why?"
- acknowledge and talk openly about the loss and the suicide
- use the name of the person who killed himself and the word "suicide."
- help the survivor say "good-bye" to the person who has died, when they are ready

- help the survivor develop a new relationship (of memory) with that person
- encourage the bereaved to take an active role in their healing and recovery
- facilitate reinvestment in relationships, activities and future plans
- encourage and assist the survivor to identify and use supports and services
- facilitate links with professional help when needed
- give time for healing

Finally, watchfulness or vigilance about suicide risk is essential. For some survivors, thoughts of suicide and suicidal acts are part of their response to the loss. Caregivers need to be willing to ask about suicide and to respond appropriately.

Using Evaluation — A Case Study

LivingWorks grew out of the recognition that more was known in the suicide literature than was being used. There was a body of clinical and experimental knowledge that either no one knew or knew how to transfer to caregivers. In the program evaluation literature, we found Rothman's social research and development (R&D) model for changing core knowledge into practical programs — the very thing we wanted to do. Since our earliest beginnings in the late 1970s, this model has been our template as we developed, tested and evaluated the effectiveness of our suicide prevention programs. We offer our experience as a case study in how evaluation can positively interact with program development and dissemination.

Most of the empirical evaluation on LivingWorks' programs has been directed to its *Applied Suicide Intervention Skills Training (ASIST)* workshop, the core program that presents "suicide first-aid" to

caregivers. Seven editions of the trainer learning materials have been produced, including updated videos and transparencies.

Initial evaluation within Alberta involved pilot and multiple field tests of the curriculum and of the delivery vehicle along with participant and outside expert feedback. Since the initial pilot test in 1982, all participant satisfaction evaluations are reviewed and direct feedback is returned to each Registered ASIST Trainer. Over 99% of the workshop participants endorse the value of attendance for other caregivers. A doctoral dissertation demonstrated significant improvement in specific suicide helping skills using pre- and post-videotaped and protocol-scored encounters with a simulated person at-risk.

Implementation outside Alberta occurred, nationally and internationally, with several system partners during the 1980s. Canada's federal prison system, Correctional Services Canada (CSC), commissioned several program review evaluations. The LivingWorks model was confirmed as their training standard in 1994.

In a partnership with the California State Department of Mental Health, *ASIST* was implemented statewide between 1986 and 1989, and annually renewed until 1996. The California venture generated several evaluations that demonstrated retention for up to 30 months of the behavioral competencies associated with suicide first-aid: the Risk Estimation Framework and the Suicide Intervention Model. "Caregiver" functions of recognition and referral were especially improved.

In 1996, LivingWorks and Lifeline Australia conducted field trials of the *ASIST* and Suicide Awareness programs that confirmed their portability to other regions. Australian participants showed a significant increase in readiness to intervene and attitude changes toward more effective suicide intervention practice.

In the same year, the Washington State Youth Suicide Prevention Program selected LivingWorks to conduct caregiver training for adult caregivers of youth. In a comparison study with a survey sample of the general public, *ASIST* caregivers were more likely to intervene confidently and knowledgeably. While acknowledging that differences between the general public and caregivers cannot be attributed entirely to training, the evaluators concluded that LivingWorks' *ASIST* workshops made a difference.

The impact on suicide rates of improving caregiver and community readiness and competency to intervene has only a few demonstration projects to argue for its effectiveness. In three small sites where *ASIST* saturated the community caregiver population, numbers of suicides stabilized or decreased. No large-scale field trial has reported a direct impact on incidence or rates of suicidal acts. There are numerous difficulties in designing such effectiveness tests: 1) the absence of community-wide measuring technologies for accurate and reliable reporting of suicidal acts; 2) no proximal or proxy variable to substitute for suicidal behavior; 3) the intervention is indirect as it addresses the confidence level of resource supports and not a population of persons at risk directly; 4) a (estimated) critical mass of caregivers in a community must receive the experimental treatment (*ASIST* participation). A design to address these barriers has been prepared and is available.

ASIST has demonstrated generalizability and an ability to generate community-based support networks of participants with different skills and professional orientation in several regions of the world. In 1992, the Centres for Disease Control and Injury Prevention evaluated youth suicide prevention programs and recognized the LivingWorks program as an exemplary community caregiver training program.

LivingWorks participated in the development of the United Nations/World Health Organization Guidelines which have been recognized as the foundation of the Call for Action on Suicide announced by the Surgeon-General of the United States in 1999.

With other LivingWorks programs that are coordinated and integrated with it, *ASIST* is a very strong candidate for selection as the training vehicle in any large-scale trial of the impact of caregiver and community preparation on suicide. See our website (www.livingworks.net) for documentation on the studies referred to above.

Recommended Readings

General Interest

Colt, G.H. (1991). *The enigma of suicide.* New York: Summit Books.

Hoff L.A. & Adamowski, K (1998) *Creating excellence in crisis care: A guide to effective training and program designs.* San Fransciso: Jossey Bass.

Leenaars, A.A., Wenckstern, S., Sakinofsky, I., Dyck, R.J., Kral, M.J., & Bland, R.C. (Eds.). (1998). *Suicide in Canada.* Toronto, ON: University of Toronto Press.

Maris, R.M., Berman. A.L., Silverman, M.M., et. al. (2000). *Comprehensive textbook of suicidology.* New York: Guilford Press.

Ramsay, R. & Tanney, B. (1996). *Global trends in suicide prevention: Towards the development of national strategies for suicide prevention.* Mumbai, India: Tata Inst. of Social Sciences.

Selected Populations

Ellis, T.E., & Newman, C.F. (1996). *Choosing to live: How to defeat suicide through cognitive therapy.* Oakland, CA: New Harbinger Publications

Jacobs, D.G. (Ed.) (1999). *The Harvard medical school guide to suicide assessment and intervention.* San Francisco: Jossey-Bass.

Survivors

Alexander, V. (1991). *Words I never thought to speak: Stories of life in the wake of suicide.* New York, NY: Lexington Books.

Carlson, T. (1995). *Suicide survivors handbook: A guide for the bereaved and those who wish to help them.* Duluth, MN: Benline Press.

Smolin, A. & Guinan, J. (1993). *Healing after the suicide of a loved one.* New York, NY: Simon and Schuster.

Youth and Age

Berman, A.L., & Jobes, D.A. (1991). *Adolescent suicide: Assessment and intervention.* Washington, DC: American Psychological Association.

White, J. & Jodoin, N. (June 1998). *"Before-The-Fact" interventions: A manual of best practices in youth suicide prevention.* Vancouver, BC: Suicide Prevention Information and Resource Centre of British Columbia.

Underwood, M. & Dunne-Maxim, K. (revised edition) (1997). *Managing sudden traumatic loss in the schools: New Jersey Adolescent Suicide Prevention Project.* Piscataway, NJ: UMDNJ-University Behavioral Health Care.

Canadian Association for Suicide Prevention (1994). *Recommendations for suicide prevention in schools.* Calgary, AB: Canadian Association for Suicide Prevention.

McIntosh, J.L., Santos, J. F., Hubbard, R.W., & Overholser, J.C. (1994). *Elder suicide: Research, theory, and treatment.* Washington, DC: American Psychological Association.

Community

United Nations (1996). *Prevention of suicide: Guidelines for the formulation and implementation of national strategies.* New York: United Nations Document ST/ESA/245.

Media

Penrose-Wall, J., Baume, P., & Martin, G. (1999). *Achieving the balance: A resource kit for Australian media professionals for the reporting and portrayal of suicide and mental illnesses.* Canberra, ACT: Commonwealth of Australia.

Other Resources

Organizations

American Association of Suicidology (AAS)
4201 Connecticut Avenue NW, Suite 408
Washington, DC, USA 20008
Phone: (202) 237-2280
Website: www.suicidology.org

American Foundation for Suicide Prevention
120 Wall Street, 22nd floor
New York, NY, USA 10005
Phone: (212) 363-3500
Website: www.afsp.org

Canadian Association for Suicide Prevention (CASP)
The Support Network
301-11456 Jasper Avenue
Edmonton, Alberta, Canada T5K 0M1
Phone: (780) 482-0198
Website: www.suicideprevention.ca/

International Association for Suicide Prevention (IASP)
Prof. David Clark, Central Administrative Office
Rush Centre for Suicide Research and Prevention
1725 West Harrison Street, Suite 955
Chicago, IL, USA 60612-3824
Phone: (312) 942-7208
E-mail: IASP@aol.com

Suicide Prevention Advocacy Network (SPAN)
1025 Vermont Avenue NW
Washington, DC, USA 20005
Phone: (202) 449-3600
Website: www.spanusa.org

Suicide Prevention Australia (SPA)
P.O. Box K 998, Haymarket
Haymarket, NSW, Australia 2000
Phone: (612) 9568 3111
Website: www.suicidepreventionaust.org/

Library and Resource Groups

Centre for Suicide Prevention (CSP)
Suicide Information and Education Collection (SIEC)
320, 1202 Centre Street SE
Calgary, AB, Canada T2G 5A5
Phone: (403) 245-3900
Website: www.suicideinfo.ca/

Centre de Recherche et d'intervention sur le suicide et l'euthanasie (CRISE)
University of Quebec at Montreal
Montreal, Canada
Phone: (514) 987-3000, ext. 1685
Website: www.crise.ca/fr/index.asp

Australian Institute for Suicide Research and Prevention (AISRP)
Griffith University
Brisbane, QLD, Australia 4111
Phone: (617) 3875 3377
Website: www.griffith.edu.au/school/psy/aisrap/

Suicide Prevention Resource Center (SPRC)
55 Chapel Street
Newton, MA, USA 02458-1060
Phone: (887) 438-7772
Website: www.sprc.org

Suicide Research and Prevention Unit
University of Oslo
Oslo, Norway
Website: www.med.uio.no/ipsy/ssff/hovedengelsk.htm

Journals

Suicide and Life-Threatening Behavior (AAS)
Crisis (IASP)
Current Awareness Bulletin (SIEC)
Archives of Suicide Research (IASR)
Phone: 31 78 639 21 34
Website: www.wkap.nl

Invitations to Help

Learn about **SITUATIONS**

- relationship problems
- work problems/failing grades
- trouble with the law
- recent suicide and violence, much publicized

almost anything depending upon how the person feels about it

Ask about **PHYSICAL CHANGES**

- lack of interest/pleasure in all things
- lack of physical energy
- disturbed sleep
- change/loss of sexual interest
- change/loss of appetite, weight
- physical health complaints

Observe **BEHAVIORS**

- crying
- emotional outbursts
- alcohol/drug misuse
- recklessness
- fighting/law breaking
- withdrawal
- dropping out
- prior suicidal behavior
- putting affairs in order

Listen for **THOUGHTS**

- escape
- no future
- guilty
- alone
- damaged
- helpless
- preoccupied
- talk of suicide or death
- planning for suicide

Sense **FEELINGS**

- desperate
- angry
- sad
- ashamed
- worthless
- lonely
- disconnected
- hopeless

quick reference

Invitations To Help

Stress

A person's interest in talking about life events could be an invitation to help prevent suicide. Disruptive life events, particularly those experienced as an intolerable loss, may be accompanied by thoughts of suicide. A loss that seems trivial to an adult can be a life-threatening crisis for an adolescent. To determine the severity of a life event, ask about the person's feelings about and view of the loss.

Ask: *How are you feeling about the things that have happened to you?*

Reactions

Changes in behavior, physical condition, thoughts, or feelings can also be invitations to help. The more that symptoms convey themes of hopelessness, helplessness and isolation, the greater the likelihood that thoughts of suicide may be involved. To find out if this theme is present, ask the person.

Ask: *Sounds like you might be feeling hopeless [helpless, alone] right now. Is that correct?*

Thoughts of Suicide

Thoughts of suicide are the clearest invitations to help prevent suicide. These thoughts may not be directly or openly stated. When they are, they are often stated in a roundabout or indirect way. To find out if a person is thinking about suicide, ask.

Ask: *Are you thinking about suicide? Are you planning on killing yourself?*

Risk Review

Current Suicide Plan

A suicide plan includes choice of a method, preparation to carry out the plan, and a time frame for completing the act. When asked directly, most people who are thinking about suicide will openly and honestly share the details of their plans. The more detailed the plan, the greater is the risk that the plan may be carried out. If the person will not tell you the details of his plan, assume that he has planned in great detail.

Ask: *Have you thought about how and when you would do it? What have you done about carrying out your plan?*

Pain

People with intolerable pain are desperate to end it. Desperation causes anything that might relieve the pain, including suicide, to happen more quickly. Persons who feel less pain or who believe that they have more ways to control their pain are less likely to act quickly. Ask about the person at risk's view of their pain.

Ask: *Do you have pain that at times feels unbearable?*

Resources

Personal support systems can sustain an individual in times of great personal troubles. Resources might include a satisfactory job; adequate finances; a place to live; caring family or friends; access to psychological or medical help; or memberships in churches, clubs, or other social institutions. Supportive resources can effectively lower the risk of suicidal behavior. The absence of supportive resources can greatly increase the risk of suicide. The person most at risk is someone who is feeling alone and unconnected to others.

In order to determine whether resources are increasing risk, ask about the person at risk's view of their resources.

Ask: *Do you feel you have few, if any, resources?*

Prior Suicidal Behavior

People who have previously tried to kill themselves are 40 times more at risk of suicide than someone who has never tried before. A prior attempt means that suicide is familiar to the person. Familiar things are more likely to be done again.

Ask: *Have you ever attempted suicide before?*

Mental Health

Persons with a history of mental health problems or those suffering currently with a mental health problem are far more likely to die by suicide or to harm themselves than those who do not have these problems. If the person answers "yes" to the following question, assume that they are more vulnerable to suicide.

Ask: *Are you receiving or have you received mental health care?*

Safeplans

All Safeplans

- If thoughts of suicide are present ⫸ Keep safe
  Safety contact(s)
  Safe/no use of alcohol/drugs
  Link to resources

Risk Specific Safeplans

- If the person has prepared a suicide plan ⫸ Disable the plan

- If the person feels desperate ⫸ Ease the pain

- If the person feels alone ⫸ Link to more resources

- If the person is familiar with suicide because of previous suicidal behavior ⫸ Protect against the danger of prior suicidal behavior and/or support past survival skills

- If the person is vulnerable to suicide because of current or previous mental health concern ⫸ Link to a health worker

Intervention Tasks

Explore   *invitations to help*

Ask: *How are you feeling about the things that have happened to you?*

Ask   about *thoughts of suicide*

Ask: *Are you thinking about suicide? Are you planning to kill yourself?*

Listen   to the *reasons for dying* and for the *reasons for living*

Ask: *Part of you feels suicide is the only answer, but another part wants to find another solution. Do I understand correctly?*

Review   *risk* factors

Ask: *I see X, Y and Z being risk alerts for you. Does that fit with how you are feeling?*

Contract   a *safeplan*

Ask: *Are we agreed then that you will do a, b, and c, and I will do x and y to prevent the immediate risk of harming yourself?*

Follow-up   on the *commitments* to the safeplan

Ask: *How do we check back with each other or with other resources to make sure everything is done?*

Helpers in Your Community

(Fill in information for your area)

Crisis (Distress) Center

Suicide Prevention Center

Teen Line

Rape/Sexual Assault Center

Domestic Violence Hotline

Sexual Abuse Hotline

Child Abuse Hotline

Police

Paramedic Emergency Medical Services Unit

Mental Health Crisis

Hospital Emergency Services

Emergency Shelters

Youth Shelter

Mental Health Outreach Clinic

Children/Youth Psychiatric Clinic

Private Practitioners

Medical Clinic

AIDS Information and Testing Sites

Children's Services Offices

School Student Services

Child Care Referrals

Parent Training

Family Support Services

Self Help Groups

Substance Abuse Counseling

Alcoholics Anonymous

Mental Health Association

Religious/Spiritual Support

Legal Assistance/Victim-Witness Assistance

Probation Officers

Who or what might be on your own list of personal resources?

Who or what might be on others' lists of personal resources?